ENGLISH 3D™

W9-CTF-690

LANGUAGE & WRITING
PORTFOLIO

TABLE OF
CONTENTS

Welcome to English 3D

Preview the English 3D Issues by taking this survey. After you complete each Issue, check back to see if your ideas or perspectives have changed.

1 Video Games

Check the statements that you think are effects of teens playing video games.

- ☐ improved coordination
- ☐ strong problem-solving skills
- ☐ poor social skills or no friends
- ☐ violent behavior

2 School Food

What's your favorite school meal? Do you consider it healthy or junk food?

My favorite school meal is _____

I consider it (healthy/junk) _____

food because _____

_____

3 Cyberbullying

One of your friends is getting mean and insulting text messages from another student at your school. What would you do? Circle your most likely response.

1. Nothing so that the bully does not attack me.
2. Tell the bully to leave my friend alone.
3. Tell a teacher or the principal.
4. Tell an adult in my family or my friend's family.
5. Call the police.

4 Graffiti

Check the punishment that you think is appropriate for someone who paints graffiti on a building.

- ☐ a warning
- ☐ $500 fine
- ☐ 2 months in jail
- ☐ $1,000 fine and 6 months in jail

5 Girls & Sports

Boys AND girls should be allowed to participate in these sports at school. Write *A* if you agree. Write *D* if you disagree.

_____ soccer   _____ basketball

_____ football   _____ wrestling

_____ baseball   _____ volleyball

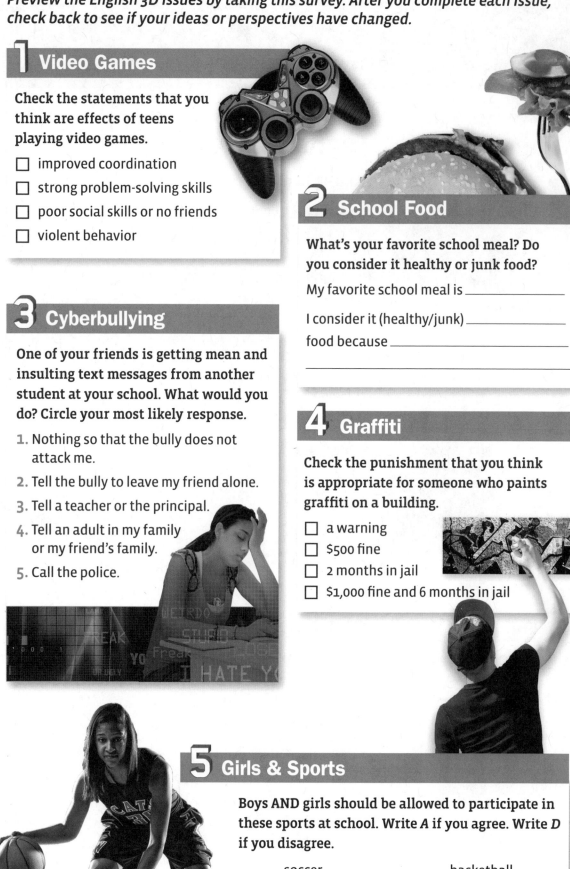
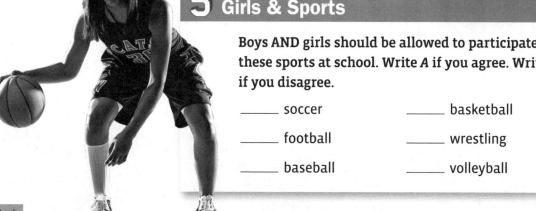

6 Animal Research

When is it okay for scientists to use animals for testing? Check any of the reasons you agree with.

☐ Testing makeup to make sure it won't cause skin problems.

☐ Testing cures for deadly diseases like cancer.

☐ Testing drugs for non-deadly conditions like headaches.

☐ Testing cleaning products like glass cleaner or wood polish.

☐ Never for any reason.

7 The Environment

Which of these materials do you recycle at home or school? Write *R* if you recycle them. Write *T* if you trash them.

_____ soda cans

_____ glass bottles

_____ plastic water bottles

_____ plastic bags

_____ paper

8 Teens & Driving

What do you know about teens and driving? Write *T* for true and *F* for false.

_____ Car crashes are the number one killer of teens in the U.S.

_____ All 50 states require teens to attend school to get a driver's license.

_____ One of the most common errors teens make while driving is being distracted by something.

9 Self-Image

How do TV, the Internet, and magazines affect you? Check any of the statements that apply.

☐ I bought something because of an ad on TV.

☐ I changed my appearance because of something I saw in a magazine.

☐ I changed my behavior because of something I read online.

10 Teens at Work

List three jobs you would be interested in having to earn money after school or during the summer.

1. _____

2. _____

3. _____

11 Drug Testing

What do you know about drug testing in schools? Write *T* for true and *F* for false.

_____ Drug testing of student athletes is against the law.

_____ Drug testing of students who participate in after-school activities is legal.

_____ Teen drug use has been on the rise since 2000.

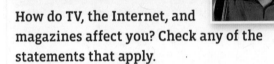

12 Social Media

How do you use social media? Check any of the statements that apply.

☐ I rarely or never use social media.

☐ I belong to one or more social media sites.

☐ I use social media sites to post photos.

☐ I use social media sites to chat with friends.

☐ I log in to a social media site every day.

☐ I have my own website.

Academic Discussion

HOW DOES A LESSON PARTNER DEMONSTRATE ACTIVE LISTENING?

BRAINSTORM IDEAS

Briefly record at least two ideas in each column using everyday English.

Physical (Body Language)	Verbal (Spoken & Written Language)
• makes eye contact • sits up straight	• waits until I have finished to share • says something positive

MAKE A CLAIM

Rewrite one idea using the academic English response frame.

Frame: I think that a lesson partner demonstrates active listening when (she/he) _____ (**present-tense verb**: permits, waits, respects, turns)

Response: _____

_____

COLLABORATE

Listen attentively, restate, and record your partner's idea.

Classmate's Name	Idea

Language to RESTATE

So you think that _____.

Yes, that's right.

No, not exactly. What I meant was _____.

PRESENT IDEAS

Listen attentively, compare ideas, and take notes. Then write whether you agree or disagree.

Language to COMPARE IDEAS

I agree with _____'s idea.

Classmate's Name	Idea	Agree/Disagree

Academic Discussion

WHAT ARE THE CHARACTERISTICS OF AN EFFECTIVE LESSON PARTNER?

BRAINSTORM IDEAS
Briefly record at least two ideas. Use precise adjectives.

Everyday	Precise
• smart	• creative, curious,
• good	• organized, focused,
• nice	• respectful, patient,
• fun	• clever, witty,

MAKE A CLAIM
Rewrite one idea using the academic English response frame and precise adjectives.

Frame: In my opinion, an effective lesson partner is _____ (**adjective:** prepared, organized) and _____ (**adjective:** respectful, creative)

Response: _____

_____

COLLABORATE
Listen attentively, restate, and record your partner's idea.

Classmate's Name	Idea

PRESENT IDEAS
Listen attentively, compare ideas, and take notes. Then write whether you agree or disagree.

Classmate's Name	Idea	Agree/Disagree

Words to Go

 BUILD WORD KNOWLEDGE

Complete the meaning and examples for this high-utility word.

Word to Go	Meaning	Examples
encourage en·cour·age *verb*	to say or do something that helps someone have more _____	A counselor should **encourage** new students to make friends by _____ _____ _____ My family **encourages** me to get to school on time by _____ _____

💬 **DISCUSS & WRITE EXAMPLES**

Discuss your response with a partner. Then complete the sentence in writing.

On reality television shows, judges **encourage** singing and dancing contestants by offering them _____

Write your response and read it aloud to a partner.

Baby-sitters often _____ spoiled children to behave better by

_____

 BUILD WORD KNOWLEDGE

Complete the meaning and examples for this high-utility word.

Word to Go	Meaning	Examples
permit per·mit *verb*	to _____ something	The school dress code does not **permit** _____ _____ A strong leader **permits** _____ _____ _____

💬 **DISCUSS & WRITE EXAMPLES**

Discuss your response with a partner. Then complete the sentence in writing.

My parents only **permit** me to _____

if _____

Write your response and read it aloud to a partner.

Our math teacher does not _____ students to _____

_____

Words to Go

 BUILD WORD KNOWLEDGE

Complete the meaning and examples for this high-utility word.

Word to Go	Meaning	Examples
contribute con·trib·ute *verb*	to add _____ or _____	I **contributed** to the discussion by _____ _____ Students might not want to **contribute** in class if they _____ _____

DISCUSS & WRITE EXAMPLES

Discuss your response with a partner. Then complete the sentence in writing.

In a group project, you can make sure everyone **contributes** by _____

_____

Write your response and read it aloud to a partner.

I have _____ to a family decision about _____

_____

BUILD WORD KNOWLEDGE

Complete the meaning and examples for this high-utility word.

Word to Go	Meaning	Examples
perspective per·spec·tive *noun*	a way of _____ about a situation	My **perspective** about drinking changed when I found out that they contain a lot of _____ At school assemblies, teachers often explain their **perspectives** on _____ _____

DISCUSS & WRITE EXAMPLES

Discuss your response with a partner. Then complete the sentence in writing.

When two friends have a misunderstanding, _____

_____

can help them understand each other's **perspective**.

Write your response and read it aloud to a partner.

When it comes to driving, parents and teens often have different

_____ about whether the child should _____

Academic Discussion

HOW CAN TEACHERS ENCOURAGE MORE STUDENTS TO CONTRIBUTE DURING CLASS DISCUSSIONS?

 BRAINSTORM IDEAS

Briefly record at least two ideas in each column using everyday English.

Before the Discussion	During the Discussion
• explain the directions clearly • build in quiet "think time"	• call on people who don't usually share • say something positive

 ANALYZE WORDS

Complete the chart with precise verbs to discuss and write about the topic.

> **Language to REPORT**
>
> One precise verb I plan to use is _____ .

Everyday	Precise
let	allow, support,
give	distribute, model,
tell	expect, require,

MAKE A CLAIM

Rewrite two ideas using the academic English response frames and precise verbs.

1. **Frame:** From my perspective, teachers can encourage more students to contribute by _____ (**verb + *ing*:** assigning, permitting, demonstrating)

   Response: _____

   _____

   _____

2. **Frame:** From my perspective, more students contribute to discussions when the teacher _____ (**present-tense verb:** explains, models, respects)

   Response: _____

   _____

   _____

Academic Discussion (continued)

COLLABORATE

Listen attentively, restate, and record your partner's idea.

Classmate's Name	Idea

Language to RESTATE

So your perspective is that _____.

Yes, that's correct.

No, not exactly. What I meant was _____.

Language to COMPARE IDEAS

I (agree/disagree) with _____'s perspective.

PRESENT IDEAS

Listen attentively, compare ideas, and take notes. Then write whether you agree or disagree.

Classmate's Name	Idea	Agree/Disagree

Words to Go

 BUILD WORD KNOWLEDGE

Complete the meanings and examples for this high-utility word.

Word to Go	Meanings	Examples
advantage ad·van·tage *noun*	something that helps you to be better or more _____; something that is good or _____ about a place, thing, or situation	In today's multicultural workplace, _____ _____ _____ is an **advantage**. An **advantage** of having a pet is _____ _____

 DISCUSS & WRITE EXAMPLES

Discuss your response with a partner. Then complete the sentence in writing.

One **advantage** of owning a smart phone is that it allows you to _____

_____

Write your response and read it aloud to a partner.

Having a part-time job is a definite _____ for high school students who want to _____

 BUILD WORD KNOWLEDGE

Complete the meaning and examples for this high-utility word.

Word to Go	Meaning	Examples
collaborative col·lab·o·ra·tive *adjective*	able to work closely with others to _____ something	Movie awards for _____ _____ are usually won by a **collaborative** team of artists. _____ classes often require more **collaborative** projects than traditional _____ classes.

 DISCUSS & WRITE EXAMPLES

Discuss your response with a partner. Then complete the sentence in writing.

One advantage of a **collaborative** project is that classmates have the opportunity to

_____

Write your response and read it aloud to a partner.

At home, one _____ chore that we all pitch in on is _____

_____

Language to Summarize

 BUILD FLUENCY
Read the article.

The Collaborative Advantage

Today, most jobs are too complex to be done by just one person. In the 21ˢᵗ century, a person who knows how to **collaborate**—to work effectively with other people—has a career **advantage**. **Collaboration** is necessary in jobs from construction to retail to medicine.

A medical trauma team is an excellent example of a **collaborative** group. Each team member has a special set of skills and responsibilities. When an accident victim arrives at a hospital, the trauma team has about one hour, known as the golden hour, to save the patient.

A team leader directs about ten doctors, nurses, and support staff. One nurse cuts off the patient's clothes. A trauma doctor examines the patient and makes a diagnosis. The radiologist **contributes** by taking x-rays. An anesthesiologist makes sure the patient is breathing and is free from pain. Another nurse calls out the patient's vital signs every five minutes.

The team interacts constantly and works with competence and confidence. No one person could save the patient alone; it takes **collaborative** teamwork.

Not all jobs are a matter of life and death. However, most jobs do require **collaboration**. If you want to succeed in a career, join the team.

ASK & ANSWER QUESTIONS
Take turns asking and answering questions with a partner.

Q: What is the **topic** of the article?

A: The **topic** of the article is _____.

Q: What are two **important details** in this article?

A: One **important detail** in this article is _____.

A: Another **important detail** in this article is _____.

Academic Discussion

WHAT ARE THE ADVANTAGES AND DISADVANTAGES OF COLLABORATIVE ASSIGNMENTS?

 BRAINSTORM IDEAS

Briefly record at least two ideas using everyday English.

Advantages	Disadvantages
• many ideas to think about • could finish faster	• more ideas to listen to • could take longer to finish

 ANALYZE WORDS

Complete the chart with precise verbs to discuss and write about the issue.

Language to REPORT

One precise verb I plan to use is _____.

Everyday	Precise
get	experience, consider,
finish	accomplish, attain,
deal (with)	tolerate, endure,

 MAKE A CLAIM

Rewrite two ideas using the academic English sentence frames and precise verbs.

1. **Frame:** In my opinion, one potential advantage of working collaboratively is being able to _____ (**base verb:** complete, brainstorm, divide)

   Response: _____

   _____

   _____

2. **Frame:** In my experience, one serious disadvantage of working in some groups is having to _____ (**base verb:** tolerate, consider, handle)

   Response: _____

   _____

   _____

Academic Discussion (continued)

COLLABORATE

Listen attentively, restate, and record your partner's idea.

Classmate's Name	Idea

Language to RESTATE

So your (opinion/experience) is that _____.

Yes, that's correct.

No, not exactly. What I meant was _____.

PRESENT IDEAS

Listen attentively, compare ideas, and take notes. Then write whether you agree or disagree.

Language to COMPARE IDEAS

My (opinion/experience) is similar to _____'s.

Classmate's Name	Idea	Agree/Disagree

Words to Go

 BUILD WORD KNOWLEDGE

Complete the meanings and examples for this high-utility word.

Word to Go	Meanings	Examples
consider con·si·der *verb*	to think about something _____ ; to have an _____ about someone or something	Due to rising gas prices, many commuters are **considering** _____ In my community, many business owners **consider** _____ _____ to be a major problem.

DISCUSS & WRITE EXAMPLES

Discuss your response with a partner. Then complete the sentence in writing.

When assigning a final grade, I think teachers should **consider** their students'

_____ in addition to their scores on assignments and tests.

Write your response and read it aloud to a partner.

When I purchase a gift for a friend or sibling, two factors I _____

are _____ and _____

 BUILD WORD KNOWLEDGE

Complete the meaning and examples for this high-utility word.

Word to Go	Meaning	Examples
productive pro·duc·tive *adjective*	_____ a lot	When students have a substitute teacher, they are typically more **productive** if their usual teacher _____ _____ A room with _____ _____ makes studying more **productive** for me.

DISCUSS & WRITE EXAMPLES

Discuss your response with a partner. Then complete the sentence in writing.

When I have an important assignment, I am usually most **productive** working in

_____ because _____

Write your response and read it aloud to a partner.

To have a _____ planning meeting for a school event, classmates

need to _____

Language to Summarize

 TAKE A SURVEY
Complete the Classroom Collaboration Survey.

 **BUILD FLUENCY**
Read the article.

Being a Team Player

Are you a natural team player who enjoys working with others? Or are you a lone wolf who prefers to work independently? No matter what kind of person you are, everyone can strive to be a more effective team member.

A construction crew is a group of people all working for the same goal: to construct a solid building that satisfies a client. However, problems often come up. For example, a construction crew might have to work around a beautiful, old tree that the client wants to save. The backhoe driver cannot move his machine easily around the tree. He wants to bulldoze it down. How can the crew solve this problem?

Productive team members have to express their own ideas clearly and listen attentively to the **perspectives** of others. They have to **consider** other approaches to the problem and be willing to compromise. They have to put the project ahead of their own personal feelings.

In the case of the construction crew, the backhoe driver and the architect compromise to come up with a new solution that saves the tree. No one loses. The team wins.

How was the problem resolved? It took skilled communication and **collaboration**.

 ASK & ANSWER QUESTIONS
Take turns asking and answering questions with a partner.

Q: What is this article **mainly about**?

A: This article is **mainly about** _____.

Q: What are the **most important details** in this article?

A: One **important detail** in this article is _____.

A: Another **important detail** in this article is _____.

Build Knowledge

IS TECHNOLOGY NEGATIVELY AFFECTING TEEN COMMUNICATION?

BRAINSTORM IDEAS
List various ways in which 21st century teens communicate.

COMMUNICATION

ELECTRONIC

• texting
• _____
• _____
• _____

WRITTEN

• notes
• _____
• _____
• _____

VERBAL

• chatting at lunch
• _____
• _____
• _____

PRESENT IDEAS
Use the academic sentence frames to write ideas and share them with your group.

1. **Frame:** A widespread form of electronic communication for teens is _____.

   Example: A widespread form of electronic communication for teens is texting.

   Response: _____

   _____

   _____

2. **Frame:** One traditional means of written communication for teens is _____.

   Example: One traditional means of written communication for teens is writing notes.

   Response: _____

   _____

   _____

3. **Frame:** Teens communicate verbally when they _____.

   Example: Teens communicate verbally when they have conversations at lunch.

   Response: _____

   _____

   _____

Words to Go

BUILD WORD KNOWLEDGE

Complete the meaning and examples for this high-utility word.

Word to Go	Meaning	Examples
competent com·pe·tent *adjective*	having enough _____ or knowledge to do something well	Becoming a **competent** soccer player requires _____ _____ Employers often look for job applicants who are **competent** users of _____ _____

DISCUSS & WRITE EXAMPLES

Discuss your response with a partner. Then complete the sentence in writing.

The most reliable way for teens to become **competent** drivers is to _____ _____

because _____

Write your response and read it aloud to a partner.

One of the most noticeable characteristics of a _____ leader is the ability to _____

BUILD WORD KNOWLEDGE

Complete the meaning and examples for this high-utility word.

Word to Go	Meaning	Examples
complex com·plex *adjective*	having many parts or details and often _____ to understand	The rules of some video games are too **complex** for most _____ Science textbooks tend to be more **complex** than other books because they include a lot of _____ _____

DISCUSS & WRITE EXAMPLES

Discuss your response with a partner. Then complete the sentence in writing.

Adults often have to ask children for assistance with using _____ _____ because they can be quite **complex**.

Write your response and read it aloud to a partner.

From my perspective, _____ is a musician who sings interesting and **complex** lyrics, such as those in the song _____

Language to Summarize

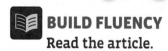 **BUILD FLUENCY**
Read the article.

The Importance of Face-to-Face Communication

You can probably text, email, blog, and tweet without a problem. But are you equally comfortable with face-to-face communication? Working with a team requires a great deal of face time with other team members. **Collaboration** is challenging if you are not sure how to communicate.

How do **competent** communicators behave? Here is an example. A school club wants to sell snacks at a weekend event. Some members of the club want to sell junk food because kids like it. Others want to try healthier alternatives. Each group presents their side of the issue at a meeting.

When the first side speaks, they present facts as well as feelings. They give reasons and evidence for their **perspectives**. Their body language is calm and confident. As they listen, the second side takes notes and looks for ideas that they agree with as well as disagree with. They respond with questions and their own opinions. They do not react with feelings and criticism. They do not explode, shut down, or ridicule.

The communication leads to a compromise that satisfies both sides. The club members avoid conflict. Communication helps the team work **productively** and find the best solution.

Use these tips for successful teamwork.
- Present your ideas effectively.
- Listen attentively to others' ideas.
- Prepare to compromise to solve **complex** problems.
- Remember your team's goal—and make it a success.

 ASK & ANSWER QUESTIONS
Take turns asking and answering questions with a partner.

Q: What is this article **mainly about**?

A: This article is **mainly about** _____.

Q: What are the **most important details** in this article?

A: One **important detail** in this article is _____.

A: Another **important detail** in this article is _____.

Academic Discussion

IS TECHNOLOGY NEGATIVELY AFFECTING TEEN COMMUNICATION?

BRAINSTORM IDEAS

Briefly record at least two ideas using everyday English.

Agree	Disagree

ANALYZE WORDS

Complete the chart with precise adjectives to discuss and write about the issue.

Language to REPORT

One precise adjective I plan to use to describe _____ is _____.

Everyday	Precise
quick	efficient, immediate,
boring	inefficient, tedious,
casual	informal, common,
fancy	formal, appropriate,

MAKE A CLAIM

Rewrite one idea using the academic English response frame and precise adjectives.

Frame: In my opinion, _____ (**form of technology:** texting, social networking, email) technology has made teen communication (more/less) _____ (**adjective:** effective, impressive, imprecise, informal)

Response: _____

_____

_____

Academic Discussion (continued)

 COLLABORATE

Listen attentively, restate, and record your partner's idea.

Classmate's Name	Idea

Language to RESTATE

So your perspective is that _____.

Yes, that's correct.

No, not exactly. What I meant was _____.

PRESENT IDEAS

Listen attentively, compare ideas, and take notes. Then write whether you agree or disagree.

Language to COMPARE IDEAS

I (agree/disagree) with _____'s perspective that _____.

Classmate's Name	Idea	Agree/Disagree

Ten-Minute Paper

✎ ELABORATE IN WRITING

Read and analyze the teacher's ten-minute paper. Circle three precise adjectives.

> In my opinion, email has made teen communication more efficient. For example, if absent students have questions about a major assignment, they can quickly send a message to a responsible classmate instead of interrupting his or her studies with a phone call. As a result, the classmate can simply reply with a brief message explaining the homework instructions rather than taking the time to go into extensive detail in a phone conversation.

Work with the teacher to write a ten-minute paper. Include two precise adjectives.

Language to REPORT
One precise word I included is _____ .

> In my opinion, texting has made teen communication less precise. For example, texting requires use of _____ vocabulary that everyone will understand and abbreviations for _____ expressions, such as _____ for _____ As a result, English teachers have noticed an increase in inappropriate _____ , spelling _____ , and texting expressions in their students' formal _____

Work with a partner to write a ten-minute paper. Include two precise adjectives.

> In my opinion, _____ has made teen communication (less/more) _____ (adjective) _____ For example, _____ _____ _____ As a result, _____ _____ _____

Are video games a brain drain—or a great way to train your brain?

BUILD KNOWLEDGE

Read and respond to the Data File (*Issues,* p. 4).

BRAINSTORM IDEAS

Complete a concept map about how teens play video games.

- alone, on a computer or gaming console

WAYS THAT TEENS PLAY VIDEO GAMES

PRESENT IDEAS

Use the frames to share ideas with your small group.

- One way that teens play video games is _____.
- Teens also play video games (in/with/by) _____.
- My favorite way to play video games is _____.

Words to Know

 BUILD WORD KNOWLEDGE

Rate your word knowledge. Then complete the chart for each topic-related word.

	① Don't Know	② Recognize	③ Familiar	④ Know

Word to Know	Meaning	Example
ability *noun* ① ② ③ ④	something that _____ _____ _____	The quarterback's **ability** to throw the ball well helped his team _____ _____
addiction *noun* ① ② ③ ④	the physical or emotional _____ _____ on a regular basis	A person who has an **addiction** to _____ risks losing _____ _____
coordination *noun* ① ② ③ ④	the ability to use _____ _____ _____ so that they _____ _____	You need good **coordination** between your _____ to _____ _____ _____
distract *verb* ① ② ③ ④	to take _____ _____ away from _____ _____	_____ _____ _____ can **distract** someone who is driving.
entertainment *noun* ① ② ③ ④	something people _____ _____ to _____ themselves	I wonder if _____ will provide **entertainment** at _____ _____ _____
interactive *adjective* ① ② ③ ④	referring to technology that can _____ _____ _____ _____	The **interactive** feature on the _____ _____ allows you to _____ _____ _____
social *adjective* ① ② ③ ④	relating to the way people _____ with _____	I think that my classmate _____ _____ has strong **social** skills.
violent *adjective* ① ② ③ ④	involving actions that are likely to _____ _____	Thousands of people _____ _____ as a result of the **violent** tsunami.

Academic Discussion
Are video games harmful or beneficial?

 BRAINSTORM IDEAS

Briefly record at least two ideas.

Harmful	Beneficial

 ANALYZE WORDS

Complete the chart with precise words to discuss and write about the issue.

Everyday	Precise
help	encourage,
waste time	avoid,
fun	entertaining,

MAKE A CLAIM

Rewrite two ideas using the frames and precise words.

1. **Frame:** I think that video games (benefit/harm) teens because they are _____ (**adjective:** enjoyable, distracting) and _____ (**adjective:** relaxing, violent)

   Response: _____

   _____

2. **Frame:** Based on my experience, video games are (beneficial/harmful) if they _____ (**present-tense verb:** contain, encourage)

   Response: _____

   _____

 COLLABORATE

Listen attentively, restate, and record your partner's idea.

Classmate's Name	Idea

Language to RESTATE

So you think
that _____.

Yes, that's right.

No, not really. What I
meant was _____.

Ten-Minute Paper

 PRESENT IDEAS
Listen attentively, compare ideas, and take notes.
Then write whether you agree or disagree.

Language to COMPARE IDEAS

I agree with _____'s idea.

Classmate's Name	Idea	Agree/Disagree

ELABORATE IN WRITING
Follow along with the teacher to write a ten-minute paper.

Based on my experience, video games are harmful if they encourage teens to procrastinate when they have something important to do. In the past, I played video games instead of _____

_____

As a result, I was forced to _____

_____

_____

_____

Work with the teacher to write a ten-minute paper.

Based on my experience, video games are _____ if they encourage teens to _____

_____

_____

In the past, I _____

_____

_____

As a result, I _____

_____

_____

Words to Go

 BUILD WORD KNOWLEDGE

Complete the meanings and examples for this high-utility word.

Word to Go	Meanings	Examples
influence in·flu·ence *noun* in·flu·ence *verb*	the power that someone or something has to _____ ; to _____ what someone does, says, or believes	A student council member might use his or her **influence** to _____ _____ _____ Residents **influenced** the mayor to _____ _____ _____

 DISCUSS & WRITE EXAMPLES

Discuss your response with a partner. Then complete the sentence in writing.

_____ had a strong **influence** on my decision to

_____

Write your response and read it aloud to a partner.

I have _____ my friends by recommending that they _____

_____

BUILD WORD KNOWLEDGE

Complete the meaning and examples for this high-utility word.

Word to Go	Meaning	Examples
evidence ev·i·dence *noun*	facts, information, or signs that show that something is _____	The fact that _____ _____ is **evidence** that someone was in my room. I would need strong **evidence** before I accused someone of _____ _____

DISCUSS & WRITE EXAMPLES

Discuss your response with a partner. Then complete the sentence in writing.

_____ is one piece of **evidence** a writer

might include in _____

Write your response and read it aloud to a partner.

_____

is _____ that I have improved my study habits.

Language to Summarize

📖 **BUILD FLUENCY**
Read the article introduction and Section 1 (*Issues*, pp. 5–6).

💬 **ASK & ANSWER QUESTIONS**
Take turns asking and answering questions with a partner.

Q: What is the **topic** of this section of the article?

A: The **topic** of this section of the article is _____.

Q: What are the **most important details** in this section?

A: One **important detail** in this section is _____.

A: Another **important detail** in this section is _____.

Section Shrink

✏️ **SUMMARIZE**
Complete the topic and important details for Section 1. Then "shrink" the section by writing a summary in 35 or fewer words.

Topic (Who?/What?):   how video games affect the brain

Important Details: • The brain releases _____

when people play video games.

• About 8.5% of teens experience _____

_____

• Evidence shows that video games can help the brain strengthen

_____ and

_____

Partner Summary: Studies have shown that video games affect the brain negatively by

_____

_____

and positively by _____

_____

Word Count: _____

Class Summary: _____

_____

_____

_____

_____

Word Count: _____

Words to Go

 BUILD WORD KNOWLEDGE

Complete the meanings and examples for this high-utility word.

Word to Go	Meanings	Examples
benefit ben·e·fit *verb* ben·e·fit *noun*	to _____ or be _____ by something or someone; something that is helpful or _____ for you	Teens might **benefit** from starting the school day later because _____ _____ One **benefit** to volunteering at an animal shelter is that _____ _____ _____

 DISCUSS EXAMPLES

Discuss your response with a partner. Then complete the sentence in writing.

Students would **benefit** if our school _____

_____

 BUILD WORD KNOWLEDGE

Complete the meaning and examples for this high-utility word.

Word to Go	Meaning	Examples
beneficial ben·e·fi·cial *adjective*	having a _____ or _____ effect on something	Using a spell check tool is **beneficial** to your writing because it _____ _____ _____ Many teens find that _____ _____ is a **beneficial** way to prepare for getting a driver's license.

 DISCUSS EXAMPLES

Discuss your response with a partner. Then complete the sentence in writing.

(A/An) _____ is a **beneficial** purchase for your cell phone because

it helps you _____

 WRITE EXAMPLES

Write your response and read it aloud to a partner.

Installing _____ would _____ our school because it

would _____

One _____ change you can make to your morning routine is to

_____

Language to Summarize

BUILD FLUENCY

Read Section 2 of the article (*Issues,* pp. 6–7).

ASK & ANSWER QUESTIONS

Take turns asking and answering questions with a partner.

Q: What is the author's **main idea**?

A: The author's **main idea** is _____.

Q: What are the **most important details** in this section?

A: One **important detail** in this section is _____.

A: Another **important detail** in this section is _____.

Section Shrink

SUMMARIZE

Complete the topic and important details for Section 2. Then "shrink" the section by writing a summary in 35 or fewer words.

Topic (Who?/What?):   the _____ effects of video games

Important Details: • Critics argue that video games _____

     _____

     • Supporters say video games benefit teens' _____

     _____

     • The majority of teens play video games _____

     _____

     • _____

Partner Summary: Critics claim that video games _____

     _____

     while supporters argue that _____

     _____

Word Count: _____

Class Summary: _____

     _____

     _____

     _____

     _____

Word Count: _____

Words to Go

BUILD WORD KNOWLEDGE
Complete the meaning and examples for this high-utility word.

Word to Go	Meaning	Examples
issue is·sue *noun*	a _____ or problem	The members of the student council debated the **issue** of _____ _____ In my opinion, **issues** concerning _____ _____ _____ should be discussed more often in our community.

DISCUSS & WRITE EXAMPLES
Discuss your response with a partner. Then complete the sentence in writing.

An **issue** that affects teens who want to _____

is _____

Write your response and read it aloud to a partner.

Of all the _____ raised by technology, I worry most about _____

_____

BUILD WORD KNOWLEDGE
Complete the meaning and examples for this high-utility word.

Word to Go	Meaning	Examples
significant sig·nif·i·cant *adjective*	large or _____ enough to have an effect on something	Professional musicians spend a **significant** amount of time _____ _____ My vacation was **significant** because _____ _____

DISCUSS & WRITE EXAMPLES
Discuss your response with a partner. Then complete the sentence in writing.

In my opinion, the most **significant** event that has happened to me this year is _____

_____

Write your response and read it aloud to a partner.

One _____ part of a lifeguard's job is _____

_____

Quote Quest

BUILD FLUENCY
Read Section 3 of the article (*Issues*, pp. 8–9).

ANALYZE TEXT
Choose and record a quote that either supports or contradicts your position. Then use a frame to paraphrase the quote.

Quote: _____

_____

_____

_____

Paraphrase: _____

_____

_____

> **Language to PARAPHRASE**
>
> I think this means that _____.
>
> To me, this means that _____.

SYNTHESIZE IDEAS
Write a topic sentence and two supporting sentences to respond to the quote.

Topic Sentence: I (agree/disagree) with the statement that _____.

_____

_____

_____

Supporting Sentence 1: (For example,/Drawing from my own experience,) _____.

_____

_____

_____

Supporting Sentence 2: (As a result,/Consequently,) _____.

_____

_____

_____

COLLABORATE
Listen attentively as each member of your group reads a quote aloud. Then take turns using a frame to respond.

> **Language to RESPOND**
>
> I (agree/disagree) with this statement.
>
> This statement interested me.
>
> This quote surprised me.
>
> This quote bothered me.

Student Writing Model

Academic Writing Type

A **justification** states a claim and supports it with logical reasons and relevant evidence. Evidence can include information from a text and examples from personal experience.

 A. The **topic sentence** clearly states the writer's claim about the issue.
 B. **Detail sentences** support the claim with reasons and evidence from the text and the writer's experiences.
 C. The **concluding sentence** restates the writer's claim about the issue.

ANALYZE TEXT
Read this student model to analyze the elements of a justification.

> **A** After reading the article, I am convinced that video games can cause teens significant harm. **B** One reason is that games can be addictive and distract teens from more important things. For example, one of my friends plays her favorite video game from the moment she gets home from school until she goes to bed. Additionally, the article points out that many video games contain violent scenes. This is important because playing violent games can influence teens' behavior and make them more aggressive. **C** For these reasons, I maintain the position that video games are not beneficial to teens.

 MARK & DISCUSS ELEMENTS
Mark the justification elements and use the frames to discuss them with your partner.

1. **Underline the writer's claim within the topic sentence.** *The topic sentence of a justification includes* _____.

2. **Check two reasons and two pieces of evidence that support the writer's claim.** *One (reason/piece of evidence) that supports the writer's claim is* _____.

3. **Box four transition words or phrases.** *One transition (word/phrase) is* _____.

4. **Circle two verbs that express the writer's opinion.** *One verb that expresses the writer's opinion is* _____.

5. **Star four precise topic words.** *An example of a precise topic word is* _____.

Choose Language for Writing

Prompt	Are video games harmful or beneficial? Write a justification that states and supports your claim.

IDENTIFY PRECISE WORDS

Review the article to identify precise words and phrases for your justification.

Introduction	Section 1	Section 2	Section 3
• virtual world	• technology	• anti-social	• aggression
• accomplish	• chemical	• stereotype	• _____
• in control	• hard-wired	• _____	• _____
• _____	• _____	• _____	• _____
• _____	• _____	• _____	• _____
• _____	• _____	• _____	• _____

Organize Supporting Evidence

TAKE NOTES

Describe your claim about whether video games are harmful or beneficial.

My claim: I think that video games are (harmful/beneficial) _____

because _____

_____

Use academic language to restate your claim and write a topic sentence.

Topic Sentence: After reading the article, I (believe, agree/disagree, am/am not convinced)

_____ that _____

_____

List two reasons that support your claim and give evidence for each reason. You can draw from the text, your experience, or a classmate's experience.

Reason 1: _____

_____

Evidence: _____

_____

_____

Reason 2: _____

_____

Evidence: _____

_____

_____

First-Person, Present-Tense Verbs

Guidelines for Using First-Person, Present-Tense Verbs

Use a first-person singular verb whenever you use the first-person subject *I*. Use the **present tense** when you describe something that is happening now or that happens all the time.

Topic Sentence: Use a first-person, present-tense verb to state your claim. Remember to follow forms of the verb *to be* with an adjective.

>   *I believe* ...   *I feel* ...   *I disagree* ...   *I am convinced* ...

Reason/Evidence: Use a first-person, present-tense verb to describe an action you do often.

>   *I own many games.*   *I talk to my friends.*   *I do my homework first.*

Concluding Sentence: Use a first-person, present-tense verb to restate your claim. Remember to follow forms of the verb *to be* with an adjective.

>   *I conclude* ...   *I restate* ...   *I maintain* ...   *I am certain* ...

 IDENTIFY FIRST-PERSON VERBS

Read the justification and circle the first-person, present-tense verbs.

> After reading the online news story, I contend that video games can actually be good for your health. One reason is that video games have begun to combine technology and fitness. For example, I play "Dance Mania" all the time, and after a few games I feel like I just ran a mile. Additionally, the news story discusses evidence that video games can sharpen people's vision. This is important because I am nearsighted, and the fact that playing action games might help me improve my eyesight makes them even more fun. For these reasons, I reject the position that video games are an unhealthy form of entertainment.

 WRITE FIRST-PERSON VERBS

Use first-person, present-tense verbs to complete the sentences.

1. I _____ in a video game-sharing club with my friends.

2. Each month, I _____ one of my video games to a club member and borrow a game from another member.

3. At each meeting, I _____ my friends to see who can get the highest score on the game of the month.

4. In my opinion, I _____ from the club because I _____ less money on video games than I normally would.

Verbs to Express Opinions

Opinion	Verbs to Express an Opinion	Justification Examples
agree	believe conclude contend support maintain concur	After reading the article, I **contend** that video games are not addictive if teens play them in moderation. I **support** the author's argument that video games distract teens from the real world.
disagree	contend reject maintain challenge conclude oppose	I **maintain** that the issue is not significant. After reading the text, I **reject** the idea that video games harm brain development.
undecided	am uncertain am unsure am unconvinced hesitate	Although the article includes some interesting evidence, I **am unconvinced** that violent video games should be banned.

IDENTIFY OPINION VERBS

Circle the verbs in the chart that you plan to use in your justification. Then complete each sentence with an appropriate verb to express an opinion.

1. Based on evidence in the article, I _____ the claim that video games can significantly improve the skills needed for many jobs.

2. Despite the evidence presented, I _____ that game devices should not be allowed in schools.

3. For these reasons, I _____ that video games are responsible for a high number of wrist and hand injuries.

WRITE OPINIONS

Write three sentences using verbs to express opinions. Include details from "Game On or Game Over?"

1. After reading the article, I _____ that video games are

(verb to express opinion)

_____ to teens because _____

(reason that supports your claim)

_____

2. One reason I _____ the idea that video games are

(verb to express opinion)

_____ is that _____

(reason that supports your claim)

_____

3. Based on my experience, I _____ that video games are

(verb to express opinion)

_____ because _____

(evidence from your experience)

_____

Write a Justification

Prompt | Are video games harmful or beneficial? Write a justification that states and supports your claim.

WRITE A PARAGRAPH
Use the frame to write your topic sentence, detail sentences, and concluding sentence.

A

After reading the article, I _____ that _____
(verb to agree or disagree)   (your claim)

_____

_____

_____

B

One reason is that _____
(first reason that supports your claim)

_____

_____

_____

For example, _____
(evidence from the article or your experience)

_____

_____

_____

_____

Additionally, _____
(second reason that supports your claim)

_____

_____

_____

This is important because _____
(evidence from the article or your experience)

_____

_____

_____

_____

C

For these reasons, I _____ the position that _____
(verb to agree or disagree)   (restate your claim)

_____

_____

_____

Rate Your Justification

Scoring Guide	
1	Insufficient
2	Developing
3	Sufficient
4	Exemplary

 ASSESS YOUR DRAFT

Rate your justification. Then have a partner rate it.

1. Does the topic sentence clearly state your claim?	Self	1	2	3	4
	Partner	1	2	3	4
2. Did you include strong reasons and evidence to support your claim?	Self	1	2	3	4
	Partner	1	2	3	4
3. Did you include precise topic words?	Self	1	2	3	4
	Partner	1	2	3	4
4. Did you follow *I* with present-tense singular verbs?	Self	1	2	3	4
	Partner	1	2	3	4
5. Did you use strong verbs to state and restate your claim?	Self	1	2	3	4
	Partner	1	2	3	4
6. Did you include a variety of sentences (simple, compound, complex)?	Self	1	2	3	4
	Partner	1	2	3	4

 REFLECT & REVISE

Record specific priorities and suggestions to help you and your partner revise.

(Partner) Positive Feedback: You did an effective job of (organizing/including/stating)

_____

_____

(Partner) Suggestion: Your justification would be stronger if you _____

_____

_____

(Self) Priority 1: I will revise my justification so that it _____

_____

_____

(Self) Priority 2: I also need to _____

_____

_____

✓ **CHECK & EDIT**

Use this checklist to proofread and edit your justification.

☐ Does each sentence start with a capital letter?

☐ Is each sentence complete?

☐ Each time you use *I*, is it followed by a present-tense singular verb?

☐ Are all words spelled correctly?

Junk food at school: Is it your right— or totally wrong?

BUILD KNOWLEDGE
Read and respond to the Data File (*Issues,* p. 10).

BRAINSTORM IDEAS
List examples of healthy food and junk food that students eat.

HEALTHY FOOD	JUNK FOOD
• fresh fruits	• french fries

PRESENT IDEAS
Use the frames to share ideas with your small group.

• One example of a (healthy/junk) food that students eat is _____.

• Another example of (nutritious/unhealthy) food that students eat is _____.

Words to Know

BUILD WORD KNOWLEDGE

Rate your word knowledge. Then complete the chart for each topic-related word.

	① Don't Know	② Recognize	③ Familiar	④ Know

Word to Know	Meaning	Example
appealing *adjective* ① ② ③ ④	likeable or _____	I find talking on the phone more **appealing** than _____ _____ because talking is more personal.
ban *verb* ① ② ③ ④	to say that something must not _____ _____	The students at my school will _____ _____ if the principal tries to **ban** cell phone use on campus.
calorie *noun* ① ② ③ ④	a unit of _____ produced by _____	It is important to eat enough **calories** to _____ _____ _____
epidemic *noun* ① ② ③ ④	a sudden outbreak of _____ _____ that spreads quickly	The high number of _____ makes it seem as if we are suffering from an **epidemic** of bad behavior.
expensive *adjective* ① ② ③ ④	costing _____ _____	My parents said I need to _____ to help pay for my **expensive** _____ _____
habit *noun* ① ② ③ ④	something a person does _____ , usually without thinking	My brother's extreme spending **habit** has caused him to _____ _____
nutrition *noun* ① ② ③ ④	the process of eating _____ _____	A dietician is a doctor who can educate people about exercise and good **nutrition** by _____ _____
obesity *noun* ① ② ③ ④	the condition of _____ _____ that it is dangerous	_____ who suffer from **obesity** are more likely to _____ _____

Academic Discussion
Should schools ban unhealthy food?

 BRAINSTORM IDEAS

Briefly record at least two ideas.

Agree	Disagree

 ANALYZE WORDS

Complete the chart with precise words to discuss and write about the issue.

Everyday	Precise
bad for you	harmful,
very hungry	famished,
eat	consume,

✏ **MAKE A CLAIM**

Rewrite two ideas using the frames and precise words.

1. **Frame:** Based on my experience as a _____ (**noun:** runner, consumer, diabetic), schools (should/should not) prohibit unhealthy food because students _____ (**present-tense verb:** need, are, consume, have)

   Response: _____

   _____

2. **Frame:** I think that schools (should/should not) ban unhealthy food because students (are/are not) capable of _____ (**verb + -ing:** making, spending, selecting)

   Response: _____

   _____

 COLLABORATE

Listen attentively, restate, and record your partner's idea.

Classmate's Name	Idea

Language to RESTATE

So what you're saying is that _____.

Yes, that's right.

No, not really. What I meant was _____.

Ten-Minute Paper

PRESENT IDEAS

Listen attentively, compare ideas, and take notes.
Then write whether you agree or disagree.

Classmate's Name	Idea	Agree/Disagree

ELABORATE IN WRITING

Follow along with the teacher to write a ten-minute paper.

I think that schools should ban unhealthy food because students are not capable of
changing harmful eating habits without help. For example, even when parents tell
kids that junk food is _____, they continue to _____
it. As a result, many students can _____
_____
_____
_____
_____

Work with the teacher to write a ten-minute paper.

I think that schools _____ ban unhealthy food because students
_____ capable of _____
_____
_____

For example, _____
_____
_____

As a result, _____
_____
_____
_____

Words to Go

BUILD WORD KNOWLEDGE
Complete the meaning and examples for this high-utility word.

Word to Go	Meaning	Examples
prevent pre·vent *verb*	to _____ something from happening	I _____ to **prevent** an accident when I ride my bike. You would **prevent** an argument if you could just _____ _____

DISCUSS EXAMPLES
Discuss your response with a partner. Then complete the sentence in writing.

In my opinion, the best way to **prevent** falling behind on homework is to _____

_____ because _____

BUILD WORD KNOWLEDGE
Complete the meaning and examples for this high-utility word.

Word to Go	Meaning	Examples
prevention pre·ven·tion *noun*	the act of _____ something from _____	The _____ at school are part of the new efforts at crime **prevention**. Maya is campaigning to be class president by saying she'll fight for the **prevention** of _____

DISCUSS EXAMPLES
Discuss your response with a partner. Then complete the sentence in writing.

Laws against _____

should help with the **prevention** of car accidents among teens.

WRITE EXAMPLES
Write your response and read it aloud to a partner.

I believe that more education about good nutrition will aid in the _____

of _____ .

In order to _____ harming the environment, we should all _____

_____

Language to Summarize

BUILD FLUENCY
Read the article introduction and Section 1 (*Issues*, pp. 11–12).

ASK & ANSWER QUESTIONS
Take turns asking and answering questions with a partner.

Q: What is the **topic** of this section of the article?

A: The **topic** of this section of the article is _____.

Q: What are the **most important details** in this section?

A: One **important detail** in this section is _____.

A: Another **important detail** in this section is _____.

Section Shrink

SUMMARIZE
Complete the topic and important details for Section 1. Then "shrink" the section by writing a summary in 35 or fewer words.

Topic (Who?/What?): why some people oppose junk food at school

Important Details: • Michelle Obama thinks childhood obesity is a significant issue

because _____

• Studies indicate that _____

in school can cause a student to _____

each school year.

• One study demonstrated that when California schools banned

unhealthy food, _____ became overweight.

Partner Summary: Experts have shown that consuming _____

at school can cause students to _____,

while prohibiting junk food may help _____

_____

_____

Word Count: _____

Class Summary: _____

_____

_____

_____

_____

Word Count: _____

Words to Go

 BUILD WORD KNOWLEDGE

Complete the meanings and examples for this high-utility word.

Word to Go	Meanings	Examples
available a·vail·a·ble *adjective*	_____ to get or be used; not _____ or unoccupied	Computers are **available** in most public libraries so that students can _____ _____ I was not **available** on Saturday night because I _____ _____

 DISCUSS & WRITE EXAMPLES

Discuss your response with a partner. Then complete the sentence in writing.

In my opinion, a student lounge should be **available** at our school because _____

_____

Write your response and read it aloud to a partner.

I am often _____ on weekends to _____

_____

 BUILD WORD KNOWLEDGE

Complete the meanings and examples for this high-utility word.

Word to Go	Meanings	Examples
impact im·pact *noun* im·pact *verb*	the _____ of one thing on another; to have an effect on _____	_____ had a great **impact** on Keisha's grades. I am worried that this terrible weather will **impact** _____

 DISCUSS & WRITE EXAMPLES

Discuss your response with a partner. Then complete the sentence in writing.

A major injury could **impact** the team's _____

_____

Write your response and read it aloud to a partner.

I think that watching less television can have a positive _____ on a student's

_____

Language to Summarize

BUILD FLUENCY
Read Section 2 of the article (*Issues*, pp. 12–13).

ASK & ANSWER QUESTIONS
Take turns asking and answering questions with a partner.

Q: What is the author's **main idea**?

A: The author's **main idea** is _____.

Q: What are the **most important details** in this section?

A: One **important detail** in this section is _____.

A: Another **important detail** in this section is _____.

Section Shrink

SUMMARIZE
Complete the topic and important details for Section 2. Then "shrink" the section by writing a summary in 35 or fewer words.

Topic (Who?/What?): the negative effects of schools _____

Important Details:
- Some people think banning junk food from schools will not teach students to _____
- Some students rely on vending machines to _____
  _____
- The money from school vending machines _____
  _____

Partner Summary: Opponents of a junk food ban in schools claim _____
_____.

Instead, the ban would _____

and _____

Word Count: _____

Class Summary: _____
_____
_____
_____
_____
_____

Word Count: _____

Words to Go

 BUILD WORD KNOWLEDGE

Complete the meaning and examples for this high-utility word.

Word to Go	Meaning	Examples
restrict re·strict *verb*	to _____ the size, amount, or range of something	School rules often **restrict** the way students _____ _____ Some parents **restrict** the amount of time teens spend _____ _____

DISCUSS & WRITE EXAMPLES

Discuss your response with a partner. Then complete the sentence in writing.

Having a password on your computer **restricts** how many people can _____

_____

Write your response and read it aloud to a partner.

If schools _____ what students wear to school, students would

_____

BUILD WORD KNOWLEDGE

Complete the meaning and examples for this high-utility word.

Word to Go	Meaning	Examples
select se·lect *verb*	to pick out or _____	Colleges often **select** students _____ _____ You should probably _____ _____ before you **select** a career.

DISCUSS & WRITE EXAMPLES

Discuss your response with a partner. Then complete the sentence in writing.

My parents let me **select** where our family will go on vacation, so I chose _____

_____

Write your response and read it aloud to a partner.

On social networking sites, many teens _____ friends based on

_____

_____

Quote Quest

BUILD FLUENCY
Read Section 3 of the article (*Issues*, pp. 14–15).

ANALYZE TEXT
Record a quote that either supports or contradicts your position. Then use a frame to paraphrase the quote.

Quote: _____

_____

_____

_____

Paraphrase: _____

_____

_____

Language to PARAPHRASE
To me, this means that _____.
This quote is saying that _____.

SYNTHESIZE IDEAS
Write a topic sentence and two supporting sentences to respond to the quote.

Topic Sentence: I (agree/disagree) with the statement that _____.

_____

_____

_____

Supporting Sentence 1: (For example/Drawing from my own experience), _____.

_____

_____

_____

Supporting Sentence 2: (As a result/Consequently), _____.

_____

_____

_____

_____

COLLABORATE
Listen attentively as each member of your group reads a quote aloud. Then take turns using a frame to respond.

Language to RESPOND
I (agree/disagree) with this statement.
This statement interested me as well.
This quote surprised me as well.
This quote bothered me.

Student Writing Model

Academic Writing Type

A **justification** states a claim and supports it with logical reasons and relevant evidence. Evidence can include information from a text and examples from personal experience.

   A. The **topic sentence** clearly states the writer's claim about the issue.
   B. **Detail sentences** support the claim with reasons and evidence from the text and the writer's experiences.
   C. The **concluding sentence** restates the writer's claim about the issue.

ANALYZE TEXT

Read this student model to analyze the elements of a justification.

A   After reading the article, I believe that unhealthy food should not be banned from schools. One reason is that young people need to learn how to make smart, nutritious selections.

B   For example, the health problems my uncle has suffered as a result of obesity have had a tremendous impact on the food I choose to eat. Additionally, I think students would have to rely on a snack option that is expensive or not easily available. The article points out that vending machine snacks are convenient for students who participate in after-school activities or sports. For these reasons, I

C   maintain the position that schools should not ban unhealthy food.

MARK & DISCUSS ELEMENTS

Mark the justification elements and use the frames to discuss them with your partner.

1. **Underline the writer's claim.** *The writer's claim is that _____.*

2. **Check two reasons and two pieces of evidence that support the writer's claim.** *One (reason/piece of evidence) that supports the writer's claim is _____.*

3. **Draw boxes around five transition phrases.** *One transition phrase is _____.*

4. **Circle three verbs that express the writer's opinion.** *One verb that expresses the writer's opinion is _____.*

5. **Star four precise topic words.** *An example of a precise topic word is _____.*

Choose Language for Writing

Prompt	Should schools ban unhealthy food? Write a justification that states and supports your claim.

 IDENTIFY PRECISE WORDS

Review the article to identify precise words and phrases for your justification.

Introduction	Section 1	Section 2	Section 3
• pro-health food	• habit	• banning	• responsibility
• nutrition	• behaviors	• impact	• _____
• obesity	• vending machines	• _____	• _____
• _____	• _____	• _____	• _____
• _____	• _____	• _____	• _____
• _____	• _____	• _____	• _____

Organize Supporting Evidence

 TAKE NOTES

Describe your claim about whether schools should ban unhealthy food.

My claim: I think that schools (should/should not) _____ prohibit

unhealthy food because _____

_____

Use academic language to restate your claim and write a topic sentence.

Topic Sentence: After reading the article, I (believe, agree/disagree, am/am not convinced)

_____ that _____

_____

List two reasons that support your claim and give evidence for each reason. You can draw from the article, your experience, or a classmate's experience.

Reason 1: _____

_____

Evidence: _____

_____

Reason 2: _____

_____

Evidence: _____

_____

Modal Verbs

Guidelines for Using Modal Verbs

Use **modal verbs** in your justification to describe what is possible or preferable.

The modal verb *should* tells about something you believe needs to happen.

> *In my opinion, students **should** finish high school if they want to be successful.*

The modal verb *would* tells about something you believe is possible.

> *Higher ticket prices **would** help the drama club raise money.*

The modal verb *could* tells about something that might be possible in the future.

> *Students **could** earn more money if the government raised the minimum wage.*

 IDENTIFY MODAL VERBS

Read the justification and circle the modal verbs.

After reading the editorial in the school newspaper, I agree with the statement that nutritious snacks should replace unhealthy snacks in vending machines. One reason is that a healthy snack could help students who participate in after-school programs maintain their energy until dinner. For example, I often buy a candy bar or other sugary snack before an after-school activity. The quick boost of energy that the snack provides quickly fades. The complex carbohydrates in a nutritious snack like a whole-grain granola bar would provide longer-lasting energy. As a result, students could practice music, study, or swim laps for much longer than with the candy bar. For this reason, I conclude that schools should make healthy snacks available in vending machines.

 WRITE MODAL VERBS

Write modal verbs to complete the sentences.

1. I am convinced that our school cafeteria _____ make a salad bar available to students.

2. A salad bar _____ provide students with a nutritious lunch option.

3. The salad bar _____ include healthy foods that appeal to many students.

4. Students _____ select from a variety of fruits and vegetables and develop healthier eating habits.

5. This option _____ also benefit the school cafeteria because so many students _____ buy lunch instead of bringing their own.

Transitions to Introduce Evidence

Transitions	Type of Evidence	Examples
The article points out _____. *In addition, the article states _____.* *In the article, (author's name) explains _____.* *(Author's name) emphasizes _____.*	From Text	**The article points out** that obesity is a major epidemic in young people across America. **In the article, Rodriguez explains** that the government will not fund junk food in schools.
In my experience, _____. *Based on my experience as a _____.* *Drawing from my experience as a _____.* *Within my (culture/community), _____.*	From Experience	**In my experience,** I have watched a friend eat a bag of corn chips because she thinks she is getting a serving of vegetables. **Within my culture,** young people learn to make their own choices about food at an early age.

IDENTIFY TRANSITIONS

Circle the transitions in the chart that you plan to use in your justification. Then complete each sentence below with an appropriate transition.

1. _____ that
   (Transition for Evidence From Text)
   students gain a significant amount of weight from eating junk food.

2. _____ ,
   (Transition for Evidence From Experience)
   I gained eight pounds last year from eating so much candy.

3. _____ how
   (Transition for Evidence From Text)
   a ban on junk food in California reduced the number of overweight students.

WRITE SUPPORTING EVIDENCE

Write three sentences using transitions to introduce evidence that supports your claim. Circle the type of evidence each transition introduces.

1. _____

   _____

   Evidence From Text   Evidence From Experience

2. _____

   _____

   Evidence From Text   Evidence From Experience

3. _____

   _____

   Evidence From Text   Evidence From Experience

Write a Justification

Prompt Should schools ban unhealthy food? Write a justification that states and supports your claim.

✏️ WRITE A PARAGRAPH

Use the frame to write your topic sentence, detail sentences, and concluding sentence.

A

After reading the article, I _____ that
_____(verb to agree or disagree)_____

_____
(your claim)

_____

_____

B

One reason is that _____
_____(first reason that supports your claim)_____

_____

_____

_____

_____
(Transition introducing evidence)

_____
(evidence from the article or your experience)

_____

_____

Additionally, _____
_____(second reason that supports your claim)_____

_____

_____

_____
(Transition introducing evidence)

_____
(evidence from the article or your experience)

_____

_____

C

For these reasons, I _____ the position that
_____(verb to agree or disagree)_____

_____
(restate your claim)

_____

_____

Rate Your Justification

 ASSESS YOUR DRAFT
Rate your justification. Then have a partner rate it.

Scoring Guide	
1	Insufficient
2	Developing
3	Sufficient
4	Exemplary

1. Does the topic sentence clearly state your claim?	Self	1	2	3	4
	Partner	1	2	3	4
2. Did you include strong reasons and evidence to support your claim?	Self	1	2	3	4
	Partner	1	2	3	4
3. Did you include precise topic words?	Self	1	2	3	4
	Partner	1	2	3	4
4. Did you follow I with present-tense singular verbs?	Self	1	2	3	4
	Partner	1	2	3	4
5. Did you use strong verbs to state and restate your claim?	Self	1	2	3	4
	Partner	1	2	3	4
6. Did you include transitions to introduce evidence?	Self	1	2	3	4
	Partner	1	2	3	4
7. Did you include a variety of sentences (simple, compound, complex)?	Self	1	2	3	4
	Partner	1	2	3	4

REFLECT & REVISE
Record specific priorities and suggestions to help you and your partner revise.

(Partner) Positive Feedback: You did an effective job of (organizing/including/stating)

_____

_____

(Partner) Suggestion: Your justification would be stronger if you _____

_____

_____

(Self) Priority 1: I will revise my justification so that it _____

_____

_____

(Self) Priority 2: I also need to _____

_____

_____

 CHECK & EDIT
Use this checklist to proofread and edit your summary.

☐ Does each sentence end with appropriate punctuation?

☐ Is each sentence complete?

☐ Did you use commas appropriately after transitions?

☐ Are all words spelled correctly?

30-Second Speech

IDENTIFY TOPIC

Choose one of the questions below to address in a 30-second speech.

☐ Should our school consider using video games in some classes?

☐ What is one change our school cafeteria should make?

BRAINSTORM IDEAS

Write your claim and two reasons that support it.

My Claim: _____

_____

Reason 1: _____

_____

Reason 2: _____

_____

SYNTHESIZE IDEAS

Take notes on evidence from the text or your experience that supports your claim.

Evidence 1: _____

_____

Evidence 2: _____

_____

WRITE A SPEECH

Write a 30-second speech that states your claim and includes reasons and evidence.

I think that our school should _____

_____

I believe this because _____

_____

_____

In addition, _____

_____

_____

For example, _____

_____

_____

Therefore, I firmly believe that our school should _____

_____

Present & Rate Your Speech

Using a Public Voice
A **public voice** is three times louder and two times slower than your everyday voice. People who are farther away need to hear you, and you want them to understand you the first time.

PRESENT YOUR SPEECH
Present your speech to the small group. Make sure to use a public voice.

TAKE NOTES
Listen attentively to your classmates.
Take notes and write if you agree or disagree.

Language to AFFIRM & CLARIFY

That's an interesting claim.
I have a question about _____.

Classmate's Name	Idea	Agree/ Disagree

ASSESS YOUR SPEECH
Use the Scoring Guide to rate your speech.

Scoring Guide			
1	Insufficient	3	Sufficient
2	Developing	4	Exemplary

1. Did your topic sentence clearly state your claim?	1	2	3	4
2. Did you include strong reasons and evidence to support your claim?	1	2	3	4
3. Did you include precise topic words?	1	2	3	4
4. Were you easy to understand?	1	2	3	4
5. Did you use a public voice (adequate volume and appropriate pace)?	1	2	3	4

REFLECT
Think of two ways you can improve for your next speech.

Priority 1: I can improve my next speech by _____

_____

Priority 2: When I present my next speech, I will focus on _____

_____

_____

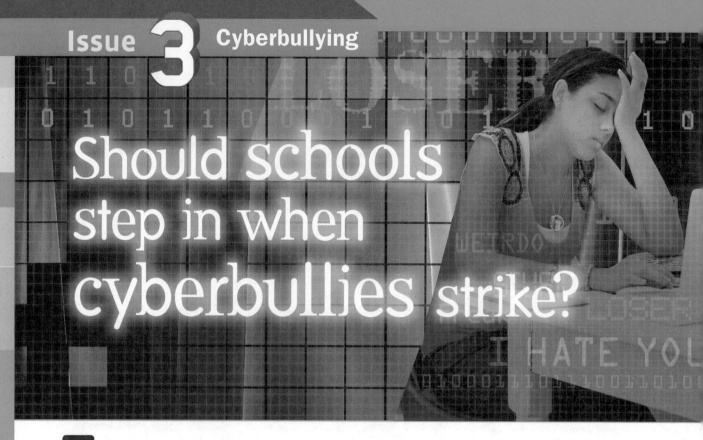

Should schools step in when cyberbullies strike?

 BUILD KNOWLEDGE
Read and respond to the Data File (*Issues,* p. 16).

 BRAINSTORM IDEAS
List similarities and differences between cyberbullying and traditional bullying.

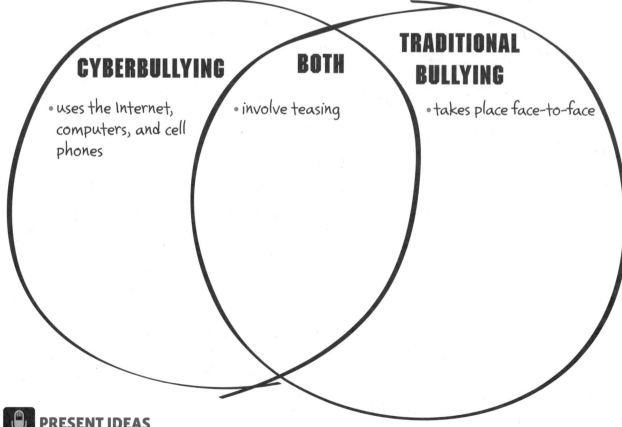

CYBERBULLYING
- uses the Internet, computers, and cell phones

BOTH
- involve teasing

TRADITIONAL BULLYING
- takes place face-to-face

PRESENT IDEAS
Use the frames to share ideas with your small group.

- One (similarity/difference) between cyberbullying and traditional bullying is _____.
- Cyberbullying _____ while traditional bullying _____.
- Cyberbullying and traditional bullying both _____.

Words to Know

BUILD WORD KNOWLEDGE

Rate your word knowledge. Then complete the chart for each topic-related word.

	① Don't Know	② Recognize	③ Familiar	④ Know

Word to Know	Meaning	Example
authority noun ① ② ③ ④	the official right or power to _____ _____	The manager of the movie theater used her **authority** and asked a group of loud teenagers _____ _____
harass verb ① ② ③ ④	to frequently _____ _____ and make his or her life unpleasant	I become angry when older kids **harass** younger ones by _____ _____ _____
responsible adjective ① ② ③ ④	having a duty to _____ _____ or look after something or someone	When _____ _____ I am **responsible** for my younger brother.
target noun ① ② ③ ④	someone or something that is chosen _____ _____	The new student was the **target** of _____ _____
technology noun ① ② ③ ④	the use of _____ _____ to do everyday tasks	My favorite new piece of **technology** is my digital notebook because it helps me to _____ _____
threat noun ① ② ③ ④	a statement that expresses the possibility that something _____ _____	The neighborhood bully made a **threat** against _____ and caused him to run home crying.
victim noun ① ② ③ ④	a person who has been injured or _____ _____	You should _____ _____ ; otherwise, you could become a **victim** of theft.
violate verb ① ② ③ ④	to do something that makes someone feel _____	When Tanya saw that _____ _____ she yelled, "No one has the right to **violate** my privacy!"

Academic Discussion

SHOULD SCHOOLS BE RESPONSIBLE FOR PUNISHING CYBERBULLIES?

BRAINSTORM IDEAS
Briefly record at least two ideas.

Agree	Disagree

ANALYZE WORDS
Complete the chart with precise words to discuss and write about the issue.

Everyday	Precise
in charge of	accountable,
bother	violate,
power	license,

MAKE A CLAIM
Rewrite two ideas using the frames and precise words.

1. **Frame:** Based on my experience with _____ (**verb + -ing:** bullying, using the Internet), _____ (**plural noun:** schools, parents, authorities) should be responsible for punishing cyberbullies.

   Response: _____

   _____

2. **Frame:** I believe that schools (should/should not) be accountable for disciplining cyberbullies when they _____ (**present-tense verb phrase:** attend the same/different schools, threaten the safety of, violate a student's right to)

   Response: _____

   _____

COLLABORATE
Listen attentively, restate, and record your partner's idea.

Classmate's Name	Idea

Language to RESTATE

So what you're suggesting is that _____.

Yes, that's right.

Actually, what I meant was _____.

Ten-Minute Paper

PRESENT IDEAS

Listen attentively, compare ideas, and take notes. Then write whether you agree or disagree.

Classmate's Name	Idea	Agree/Disagree

ELABORATE IN WRITING

Follow along with the teacher to write a ten-minute paper.

I believe that schools should not be accountable for disciplining cyberbullies when they harass others off school property. For example, a cyberbully may try to _____ someone by sending _____ messages from a parent's computer. As a result, the parents of the cyberbully _____
_____
_____
_____

Work with the teacher to write a ten-minute paper.

I believe that schools _____ be accountable for disciplining cyberbullies when they _____
_____
_____

For example, my friend _____
_____
_____

As a result, the _____
_____
_____
_____

Words to Go

 BUILD WORD KNOWLEDGE

Complete the meanings and examples for this high-utility word.

Word to Go	Meanings	Examples
affect af·fect *verb*	to _____ someone or something; to make someone have strong _____	Not getting enough sleep can **affect** _____ _____ If _____ it will negatively **affect** me.

 DISCUSS & WRITE EXAMPLES

Discuss your response with a partner. Then complete the sentence in writing.

Banning junk food from schools may **affect** students by _____

_____

Write your response and read it aloud to a partner.

Having an after-school job could _____ the amount of time I have

for _____

 BUILD WORD KNOWLEDGE

Complete the meaning and examples for this high-utility word.

Word to Go	Meaning	Examples
response re·sponse *noun*	something that is said, written, or done as a _____ _____ to something or someone	My parents' **response** when I failed an exam was to _____ Our teacher's **response** to her surprise birthday party was _____

 DISCUSS & WRITE EXAMPLES

Discuss your response with a partner. Then complete the sentence in writing.

The **response** that teachers had to the problem of cheating included _____

_____

Write your response and read it aloud to a partner.

For some teens, their _____ to the peer pressure to steal is to

_____

Language to Summarize

📖 **BUILD FLUENCY**
Read the article introduction and Section 1 (*Issues*, pp. 17–18).

💬 **ASK & ANSWER QUESTIONS**
Take turns asking and answering questions with a partner.

Q: What is the author's **main idea**?

A: The author's **main idea** is _____.

Q: What are the **most important details** in this section?

A: One **important detail** in this section is _____.

A: Another **important detail** in this section is _____.

Section Shrink

✏️ **SUMMARIZE**
Complete the topic and important details for Section 1. Then "shrink" the section by writing a summary in 35 or fewer words.

Topic (Who?/What?): schools' responsibilities and students' rights regarding off-campus cyberbullying

Important Details:
- Bullies used a social networking site to _____ before they were _____
- Many people think that schools _____ _____
- Other people support the rights of students to _____ without _____

Partner Summary: Many people believe schools have _____ to punish cyberbullies, but others respond that _____

_____

_____

_____

Word Count: _____

Class Summary: _____

_____

_____

_____

Word Count: _____

Words to Go

 BUILD WORD KNOWLEDGE

Complete the meaning and examples for this high-utility word.

Word to Go	Meaning	Examples
data da·ta *plural noun*	_____ or facts	To _____ my computer **data**, I use a backup drive. When you join a social network, you provide personal **data** such as _____ _____

DISCUSS & WRITE EXAMPLES

Discuss your response with a partner. Then complete the sentence in writing.

For my social studies project on India, I am required to show important **data**, such as

_____

_____

Write your response and read it aloud to a partner.

It would be helpful to have more _____ about _____

_____ to decide who should punish cyberbullies.

 BUILD WORD KNOWLEDGE

Complete the meanings and examples for this high-utility word.

Word to Go	Meanings	Examples
estimate es·ti·mate *verb* es·ti·mate *noun*	to _____ the size, speed, or amount of something; a guess about the size, speed, or amount of _____	I will **estimate** the number of guests at the party so that I can _____ _____ The repair shop gave me an **estimate** that _____ _____

DISCUSS & WRITE EXAMPLES

Discuss your response with a partner. Then complete the sentence in writing.

Your **estimate** about your cousin's size was accurate, so _____

_____

Write your response and read it aloud to a partner.

I _____ that my social studies project will take three more hours

to complete, based on _____

Language to Summarize

BUILD FLUENCY
Read section 2 of the article (*Issues*, pp. 18–20).

ASK & ANSWER QUESTIONS
Take turns asking and answering questions with a partner.

Q: What is this section of the article **mainly about**?

A: This section of the article is **mainly about** _____.

Q: What are the **most essential details** in this section?

A: One **essential detail** in this section is _____.

A: Another **essential detail** in this section is _____.

Section Shrink

SUMMARIZE
Complete the topic and important details for Section 2. Then "shrink" the section by writing a summary in 35 or fewer words.

Topic (Who?/What?): cyberbullying on _____

Important Details:
- Some people, such as principal Deb Socia, believe that when students use school _____ the school

  _____

- Others argue that scanning a student's computer _____

  _____

- A study about cell phone use _____

  _____

- _____

  _____

  _____

Partner Summary: Some people argue that when students use school technology or

_____

the school _____

Others believe _____

Word Count: _____

Class Summary: _____

_____

_____

Word Count: _____

Words to Go

 BUILD WORD KNOWLEDGE
Complete the meaning and examples for this high-utility word.

Word to Go	Meaning	Examples
involved in·volved *adjective*	_____ with an activity or event in some way	I try not to get **involved** in _____ _____ Carlos got **involved** with a volunteer group to _____ _____

DISCUSS & WRITE EXAMPLES
Discuss your response with a partner. Then complete the sentence in writing.

I can't get **involved** in any more _____

_____ because I am already so busy.

Write your response and read it aloud to a partner.

If you care about improving your grades, you should get _____ in

_____

BUILD WORD KNOWLEDGE
Complete the meaning and examples for this high-utility word.

Word to Go	Meaning	Examples
prohibit pro·hib·it *verb*	to _____ or not allow an action	Movie theaters **prohibit** _____ _____ during the movie. Because of the obesity epidemic, many schools now **prohibit** _____ _____

DISCUSS & WRITE EXAMPLES
Discuss your response with a partner. Then complete the sentence in writing.

To prevent violence, the law **prohibits** the sale of _____

_____

Write your response and read it aloud to a partner.

Many high schools _____ students from leaving campus during

school hours because _____

Quote Quest

BUILD FLUENCY

Read section 3 of the article (*Issues*, pp. 20–21).

ANALYZE TEXT

Record a quote that either supports or contradicts your position. Then use a frame to paraphrase the quote.

Quote: _____

_____

_____

_____

Paraphrase: _____

_____

_____

_____

Language to PARAPHRASE
This quote is saying that _____.
To put it another way, _____.

SYNTHESIZE IDEAS

Write a topic sentence and two supporting sentences to respond to the quote.

Topic Sentence: I (agree/disagree) with the statement that _____.

_____

_____

_____

Supporting Sentence 1: (For example/Drawing from my own experience), _____.

_____

_____

_____

Supporting Sentence 2: (As a result/Consequently), _____.

_____

_____

_____

COLLABORATE

Listen attentively as each member of your group reads a quote aloud. Then take turns using a frame to respond.

Language to RESPOND
This quote stood out for me as well.
This statement impressed me.
I found this quote surprising.
This statement shocked me.

Student Writing Model

Academic Writing Type

A **justification** states a claim and supports it with logical reasons and relevant evidence. Evidence can include information from a text and examples from personal experience.

- A. The **topic sentence** clearly states the writer's claim about the issue.
- B. **Detail sentences** support the claim with reasons and evidence from the text and the writer's experiences.
- C. The **concluding sentence** restates the writer's claim about the issue.

ANALYZE TEXT
Read this student model to analyze the elements of a justification.

A
The article "The New Bully at School" has convinced me that schools should not be responsible for punishing cyberbullies.

B
One powerful reason is that most cyberbullying is done off school property. For example, someone I know used her home computer to harass a teen that once bullied her. Her actions were wrong, but they had nothing to do with school. Additionally, schools cannot get involved in cyberbullying situations for legal reasons. In the article, the author emphasizes how one school lost a lawsuit when it suspended a cyberbully. Perhaps most importantly, I believe cyberbullying that does not break the law is protected by our right to free speech—even if that speech is cruel.

C
For these reasons, I contend that schools should not be accountable for disciplining cyberbullies.

MARK & DISCUSS ELEMENTS
Mark the justification elements and use the frames to discuss them with your partner.

1. **Underline the writer's claim.** *The writer's claim is that _____.*

2. **Check three reasons and two pieces of evidence that support the writer's claim.** *One (reason/piece of evidence) that supports the writer's claim is _____.*

3. **Box six transition words or phrases.** *One transition (word/phrase) is _____.*

4. **Circle three verbs that express the writer's opinion.** *One verb that expresses the writer's opinion is _____.*

5. **Star four precise topic words.** *An example of a precise topic word is _____.*

Choose Language for Writing

Prompt	Should schools be responsible for punishing cyberbullies? Write a justification that states and supports your claim.

IDENTIFY PRECISE WORDS

Review the article to identify and record precise words and phrases for your justification.

Introduction	Section 1	Section 2	Section 3
• cyberbully	• humiliated	• clear-cut issue	• suspended
• cruel	• depression	• privacy	• _____
• guilty	• off campus	• _____	• _____
• _____	• _____	• _____	• _____
• _____	• _____	• _____	• _____
• _____	• _____	• _____	• _____

Organize Supporting Evidence

TAKE NOTES

Describe your claim about schools' responsibility for punishing cyberbullies.

My claim: I believe that schools (should/should not) _____

_____

Use academic language to restate your claim and write a topic sentence.

Topic Sentence: The article (title) _____

has convinced me that _____

_____

List reasons and evidence from text or personal experience that support your claim.

Reason 1: _____

_____

Evidence: _____

_____

Reason 2: _____

_____

Evidence: _____

_____

Reason 3: _____

Evidence: _____

_____

Regular Past-Tense Verbs

Guidelines for Using Regular Past-Tense Verbs

A **regular past-tense verb** tells about an action that already happened.
Regular past-tense verbs end in –*ed*.

Use regular past-tense verbs to describe relevant evidence from your experience.

*Last year, someone I know **bothered** a classmate online.*

*I **stopped** posting on that social networking site yesterday.*

*In 2010, my friend **received** threats from a cyberbully.*

 IDENTIFY PAST-TENSE VERBS

Read the justification below and circle the regular past-tense verbs.

> The blog post, "Virtual Pain," convinced me that the problem of cyberbullying affects adults as well as teens. One powerful reason is that there are now several support groups for senior citizens who have been victims of online intimidation. In fact, I counted twenty-four senior support groups just in one city. The blog also emphasizes that more than half of the people who ask for advice on dealing with online bullies are older than 30. In my own experience, bullies targeted several adults in my family last year. My uncle actually stopped using the Internet after bullies humiliated him online. For these reasons, I contend that cyberbullying is not just a teen problem.

WRITE PAST-TENSE VERBS

Complete the sentences with the past tense of the regular verbs in parentheses.

1. Last summer, I _____ insulting messages in my email inbox. (discover)

2. Around the same time, one of my friends also received and _____ several inappropriate photos from her phone. (delete)

3. Last year, some cyberbullies _____ a group of new students at our school. (intimidate)

4. For instance, one student _____ almost an entire month of school due to his fear of the cyberbullies. (miss)

5. In the end, the cyberbullies _____ their actions and promised never to behave that way again. (regret)

Paraphrasing Text

Guidelines for Paraphrasing Text

Look for a statement in a source text that supports your claim. Then **paraphrase** it by restating the idea using precise synonyms and your own words.

Source Text	Key Words & Phrases → Precise Synonyms			Paraphrasing
Most cyberbullying is done off school property, but much of the hurt, mockery, and revenge it creates takes place at school.	most	→	the majority of	The majority of cyberbullying happens off campus, but most of the pain and humiliation it creates occurs at school.
	is done	→	happens	
	school property	→	campus	
	much	→	most	
	hurt, mockery, and revenge	→	pain and humiliation	
	takes place	→	occurs	

⊕ IDENTIFY PRECISE SYNONYMS

Read these statements and replace the words in parentheses with precise synonyms.

1. A new middle-school student in Ridgewood, New Jersey became the (target) _____ of cyberbullies who created a Facebook group to

   (humiliate) _____ him.

2. Many people say that the school has no (power) _____ to

   (discipline) _____ cyberbullies.

3. The school should (make sure) _____ that students have a

   (safe) _____ environment in which to get an education.

✎ PARAPHRASE IDEAS

Paraphrase the three statements above using your own words and phrasing.

1. The article states that _____

   _____

   _____

2. According to the article, _____

   _____

   _____

3. One point the article makes is that _____

   _____

   _____

Write a Justification

Prompt	Should schools be responsible for punishing cyberbullies? Write a justification that states and supports your claim.

✏️ WRITE A PARAGRAPH

Use the frame to write your topic sentence, detail sentences, and concluding sentence.

A

The article _____
(title)

has convinced me that _____
(your claim)

_____

B

One _____ reason is that _____
(compelling, powerful)   .(reason that supports your claim)

_____

_____

_____

For example, _____
(evidence from the article or your experience)

_____

_____

_____
(Transition introducing a reason)

_____
(reason that supports your claim)

_____

_____
(Transition introducing evidence)

_____
(evidence from the article or your experience)

_____

_____

Perhaps most importantly, _____
(the most important reason that supports your claim)

_____

_____

C

For these reasons, I _____ that _____
(verb to agree or disagree)   (restate your claim)

_____

_____

Rate Your Justification

ASSESS YOUR DRAFT
Rate your justification. Then have a partner rate it.

1. Does the topic sentence clearly state your claim?	Self	1	2	3	4
	Partner	1	2	3	4
2. Did you include strong reasons and evidence to support your claim?	Self	1	2	3	4
	Partner	1	2	3	4
3. Did you include precise topic words?	Self	1	2	3	4
	Partner	1	2	3	4
4. Did you use correct present- and past-tense verbs?	Self	1	2	3	4
	Partner	1	2	3	4
5. Did you use strong verbs to state and restate your claim?	Self	1	2	3	4
	Partner	1	2	3	4
6. Did you include transitions to introduce reasons and evidence?	Self	1	2	3	4
	Partner	1	2	3	4
7. Did you include a variety of sentences (simple, compound, complex)?	Self	1	2	3	4
	Partner	1	2	3	4

REFLECT & REVISE
Record specific priorities and suggestions to help you and your partner revise.

(Partner) Positive Feedback: You did an effective job of (organizing/including/stating)

_____

(Partner) Suggestion: Your justification would be stronger if you _____

_____

(Self) Priority 1: I will revise my justification so that it _____

_____

(Self) Priority 2: I also need to _____

_____

CHECK & EDIT
Use this checklist to proofread and edit your justification.

☐ Does each sentence end with appropriate punctuation?

☐ Is each sentence complete?

☐ Did you use present- and past-tense verbs correctly?

☐ Are all words spelled correctly?

Is graffiti VANDALISM or ART—or both?

📖 **BUILD KNOWLEDGE**
Read and respond to the Data File (*Issues,* p. 22).

💡 **BRAINSTORM IDEAS**
List types of art, qualities that describe art, and places to see art.

ART

TYPES	**QUALITIES**	**PLACES**
• sculptures	• thoughtful	• galleries
• _____	• _____	• _____
• _____	• _____	• _____
• _____	• _____	• _____
• _____	• _____	• _____
• _____	• _____	• _____
• _____	• _____	• _____

🎤 **PRESENT IDEAS**
Use the frames to share ideas with your small group.

• One type of art I have encountered is _____.

• I think that artistic works are _____.

• Art is sometimes displayed (in/at) _____.

Words to Know

 BUILD WORD KNOWLEDGE

Rate your word knowledge. Then complete the chart for each topic-related word.

① Don't Know	② Recognize	③ Familiar	④ Know

Word to Know	Meaning	Example
artistic *adjective* ① ② ③ ④	good at _____ _____; done with _____ _____	The way Tanya _____ _____ _____ shows that she is very **artistic**.
criticism *noun* ① ② ③ ④	remarks that _____ _____ _____ about someone or something	I think teens would appreciate being able to offer **criticism** about _____ _____ without getting into trouble.
deface *verb* ① ② ③ ④	to _____ _____ the way something looks	The police arrested the teens who were about to **deface** _____ _____ with _____
express *verb* ① ② ③ ④	to _____ what you are _____ _____ with words, looks, or actions	_____ use _____ _____ to **express** themselves.
political *adjective* ① ② ③ ④	relating to _____	A **political** issue that the school government should address is _____ _____ _____
rebel *noun* ① ② ③ ④	someone who _____ _____ ideas or people that he or she _____	A **rebel** might get in trouble at school by _____ _____ _____
removal *noun* ① ② ③ ④	the act of _____ _____ _____	Celia's parents threatened the removal of _____ _____ if she _____ _____
vandalism *noun* ① ② ③ ④	the _____ of purposely _____, especially public property	When I saw _____ _____ I called the police to report the **vandalism**.

Academic Discussion

Is graffiti ART or VANDALISM?

BRAINSTORM IDEAS

Briefly record at least two ideas.

Art	Vandalism

ANALYZE WORDS

Complete the chart with precise words to discuss and write about the issue.

Everyday	Precise
good at art	creative,
make ugly	mar,
say	convey,

MAKE A CLAIM

Rewrite two ideas using the frames and precise words.

1. **Frame:** Within my _____ (**noun:** family, group of friends, community), graffiti is considered (art/vandalism) because it _____ (**present-tense verb:** changes, encourages, causes)

   Response: _____

   _____

2. **Frame:** In my opinion, graffiti is (art/vandalism) if it _____ (**present-tense verb:** expresses, defaces, makes)

   Response: _____

   _____

COLLABORATE

Listen attentively, restate, and record your partner's idea.

Classmate's Name	Idea

Language to RESTATE

So your opinion is that _____.

Yes, that's right.

Actually, what I meant was _____.

Ten-Minute Paper

PRESENT IDEAS

Listen attentively, compare ideas, and take notes. Then write whether you agree or disagree.

Classmate's Name	Idea	Agree/Disagree

ELABORATE IN WRITING

Follow along with the teacher to write a ten-minute paper.

In my opinion, graffiti is vandalism if it expresses dangerous or judgmental ideas. For example, graffiti often _____ a _____ to a rival gang. As a result, that gang may _____

_____

_____

_____

_____

Work with the teacher to write a ten-minute paper.

In my opinion, graffiti is _____ if it _____

_____

_____

For example, _____

_____

_____

As a result, _____

_____

_____

_____

Words to Go

 BUILD WORD KNOWLEDGE
Complete the meanings and examples for this high-utility word.

Word to Go	Meanings	Examples
community com·mu·ni·ty *noun*	a _____ of _____ who live in an area; the area where a _____ of _____ live	I like our **community** because _____ _____ _____ The _____ in some **communities** are _____ _____

 DISCUSS & WRITE EXAMPLES
Discuss your response with a partner. Then complete the sentence in writing.

My **community** works together to _____

_____

Write your response and read it aloud to a partner.

The _____

is the best thing about our _____

 BUILD WORD KNOWLEDGE
Complete the meaning and examples for this high-utility word.

Word to Go	Meaning	Examples
represent rep·re·sent *verb*	to be a sign or mark that _____ something	At school, _____ _____ can **represent** that you are in a particular group or clique. For many teens, turning 18 **represents** _____ _____

 DISCUSS & WRITE EXAMPLES
Discuss your response with a partner. Then complete the sentence in writing.

In a text message, smiley faces and other emoticons **represent** _____

_____

Write your response and read it aloud to a partner.

After graduation, a diploma _____ a student's _____

_____

Language to Summarize

📖 BUILD FLUENCY

Read the article introduction and Section 1 (*Issues*, pp. 23–25).

💬 ASK & ANSWER QUESTIONS

Take turns asking and answering questions with a partner.

Q: What is the author's **main idea**?

A: The author's **main idea** is _____.

Q: What are the **most important details** in this section?

A: One **important detail** in this section is _____.

A: Another **important detail** in this section is _____.

Section Shrink

 SUMMARIZE

Complete the topic and important details for Section 1. Then "shrink" the section by writing a summary in 35 or fewer words.

Topic (Who?/What?): the effects of graffiti on communities

Important Details: • Critics of graffiti think that _____

_____

• Gangs use graffiti to _____ their _____

_____

• Police say that graffiti _____

_____

Partner Summary: Critics of graffiti believe it _____

_____

especially when _____

_____

Word Count: _____

Class Summary: _____

_____

_____

_____

_____

Word Count: _____

Words to Go

 BUILD WORD KNOWLEDGE
Complete the meaning and examples for this high-utility word.

Word to Go	Meaning	Examples
cultural cul·tur·al *adjective*	having to do with the _____, ideas, and beliefs of a _____ of people	My parents _____ _____ to remind us of our cultural background. One cultural celebration in my family is _____ _____

 DISCUSS & WRITE EXAMPLES
Discuss your response with a partner. Then complete the sentence in writing.

Cultural differences in a community can result in _____
_____

Write your response and read it aloud to a partner.

Most of the _____ knowledge I have about my ancestors comes from
_____

 BUILD WORD KNOWLEDGE
Complete the meanings and examples for this high-utility word.

Word to Go	Meanings	Examples
identity i·den·ti·ty *noun*	a sense of _____; a feeling of _____ to a particular group or race	Vanessa's identity as a shy student changed when _____ _____ I value my _____ because it is part of my identity as ____ _____

 DISCUSS & WRITE EXAMPLES
Discuss your response with a partner. Then complete the sentence in writing.

In the United States, we _____
_____ to show our national **identity**.

Write your response and read it aloud to a partner.

My _____
have influenced my _____

Language to Summarize

BUILD FLUENCY

Read Section 2 of the article (*Issues*, pp. 25–26).

ASK & ANSWER QUESTIONS

Take turns asking and answering questions with a partner.

Q: What is this section of the article **mainly about?**

A: This section of the article is **mainly about** _____.

Q: What are the **most essential details** in this section?

A: One **essential detail** in this section is _____.

A: Another **essential detail** in this section is _____.

Section Shrink

SUMMARIZE

Complete the topic and important details for Section 2. Then "shrink" the section by writing a summary in 35 or fewer words.

Topic (Who?/What?):   the views of _____

Important Details: • Graffiti artists believe that _____

_____

     • SAVZ, a graffiti artist, _____

_____

     • Proponents argue that graffiti _____

_____

     • _____

_____

Partner Summary: Proponents of graffiti argue that it _____

_____

and _____

Word Count: _____

Class Summary: _____

_____

_____

_____

Word Count: _____

Words to Go

 BUILD WORD KNOWLEDGE

Complete the meaning and examples for this high-utility word.

Word to Go	Meaning	Examples
interpret in·ter·pret *verb*	to determine the _____ of something	Please don't **interpret** my remarks to mean that _____ _____ _____ A teacher might ask students to interpret _____ _____

💬 **DISCUSS & WRITE EXAMPLES**

Discuss your response with a partner. Then complete the sentence in writing.

My parents **interpreted** my refusal to tell them _____

as _____

Write your response and read it aloud to a partner.

When my best friend walked right past me in the hall, I _____

his/her behavior to mean that _____

📖 **BUILD WORD KNOWLEDGE**

Complete the meaning and examples for this high-utility word.

Word to Go	Meaning	Examples
legal le·gal *adjective*	allowed by _____	_____ _____ is legal when you are accompanied by an adult. In our community, _____ _____ _____ is not legal.

💬 **DISCUSS & WRITE EXAMPLES**

Discuss your response with a partner. Then complete the sentence in writing.

I think the **legal** voting age is 18 because _____

_____

Write your response and read it aloud to a partner.

I believe that _____

should not be _____

Quote Quest

📖 **BUILD FLUENCY**
Read Section 3 of the article (*Issues*, pp. 26–27).

🔍 **ANALYZE TEXT**
Record a quote that supports or contradicts your
position. Then use a frame to paraphrase the quote.

Quote: _____

_____

_____

_____

Paraphrase: _____

_____

_____

Language to PARAPHRASE
To put it another way, _____.
This quote clarifies that _____.

✏️ **SYNTHESIZE IDEAS**
Write a topic sentence and two supporting sentences to respond to the quote.

Topic Sentence: I (agree/disagree) with the statement that _____.

_____

_____

_____

Supporting Sentence 1: (For example,/Drawing from my own experience,) _____.

_____

_____

_____

Supporting Sentence 2: (As a result,/Consequently,) _____.

_____

_____

_____

💬 **COLLABORATE**
Listen attentively as each member of your
group reads a quote aloud. Then take turns
using a frame to respond.

Language to RESPOND
This quote stood out for me as well.
This statement impressed me.
I found this quote surprising.
This statement shocked me.

Student Writing Model

Academic Writing Type

A **justification** states a claim and supports it with logical reasons and relevant evidence. Evidence can include information from a text and examples from personal experience.

    A. The **topic sentence** clearly states the writer's claim about the issue.

    B. **Detail sentences** support the claim with reasons and evidence from the text and the writer's experiences.

    C. The **concluding sentence** restates the writer's claim about the issue.

ANALYZE TEXT

Read this student model to analyze the elements of a justification.

A

The article "The Writing on the Wall" and my own relevant experiences as a member of my community lead me to conclude that graffiti is vandalism.

B

A significant reason is that much graffiti is gang-related. Based on my experience, tagging puts a community at risk because gangs use it to mark their territory. The author also emphasizes the fact that graffiti can increase crime in neighborhoods. For example, communities with graffiti sometimes contain litter and experience other types of vandalism.

An equally important point is that graffiti hurts business and property owners due to the costs of its removal.

C

Therefore, I challenge the idea that graffiti is art.

MARK & DISCUSS ELEMENTS

Mark the justification elements and use the frames to discuss them with your partner.

1. **Underline the writer's claim.** *The writer's claim is that _____.*

2. **Check three reasons and two pieces of evidence that support the writer's claim.** *One (reason/piece of evidence) that supports the writer's claim is _____.*

3. **Box six transition words or phrases.** *One transition (word/phrase) is _____.*

4. **Circle two words or phrases that express cause and effect.** *One (word/phrase) that the writer uses to express cause and effect is _____.*

5. **Star four precise topic words.** *An example of a precise topic word is _____.*

Choose Language for Writing

Prompt | Is graffiti vandalism or art? Write a justification that states and supports your claim.

IDENTIFY PRECISE WORDS

Review the article to identify precise words and phrases for your justification.

Introduction	Section 1	Section 2	Section 3
• views	• critics	• expression	• political
• intervention program	• deteriorate	• victimless crime	• _____
• vandals	• rival gang	• _____	• _____
• _____	• _____	• _____	• _____
• _____	• _____	• _____	• _____
• _____	• _____	• _____	• _____

Organize Supporting Evidence

TAKE NOTES

Describe your claim about whether graffiti is vandalism or art.

My claim: In my opinion, graffiti (is/is not) _____

_____

Use academic language to restate your claim and write a topic sentence.

Topic Sentence: The article (title) _____

and my own relevant experiences as a (relevant personal connection) _____

_____ lead me to conclude that

(your claim) _____

_____

List reasons and evidence that support your claim. You can draw from the text, your experience, or a classmate's experience.

Reason 1: _____

Evidence: _____

_____

Reason 2: _____

Evidence: _____

_____

Reason 3: _____

Evidence: _____

_____

Complex Cause & Effect Sentences

Guidelines for Expressing Cause and Effect

A **cause** is the reason something happens. An **effect** is the result, or what happens.

> *Teens eat junk food from school vending machines. Teens gain up to 14 pounds a year.*
> cause   effect

After stating an effect, use **because** or **since** to signal that the cause follows.

> *Teens gain up to 14 pounds a year **because** they eat junk food from vending machines.*
> effect   cause

Use **due to** or **as a result of** when you want to state the cause with a noun phrase.

> *Teens with after-school activities often use vending machines **due to** afternoon hunger.*
> effect   cause
> *Diabetes is a danger for teens **as a result of** poor eating habits.*
> effect   cause

State the cause first to emphasize it. Begin with **because, since, due to**, or **as a result of** and put a comma after the cause.

> ***Because** teens eat junk food from vending machines, they gain up to 14 pounds a year.*
> cause   effect

 WRITE COMPLEX SENTENCES

Combine simple sentences to create complex cause and effect sentences.

1. Obesity is an epidemic in this country. People eat too much unhealthy food.

   a) _____ because

   _____

   b) Because _____

   _____

2. Some students suffer from depression. Students are harassed by cyberbullies.

   a) _____ due to

   _____

   b) Due to _____

   _____

3. Video games can be addictive. Some gamers think about video games constantly.

   a) _____ since

   _____

   b) Since _____

   _____

4. A man sued his daughter's school. The school suspended the girl for off-campus cyberbullying.

   a) _____ as a result of

   _____

   b) As a result of _____

   _____

Language for Quantity & Frequency

Reason (Why?)	Quantity (How Many?)	Frequency (How Often?)	Examples
because since due to as a result of	few some several many nearly all most every	never rarely occasionally frequently regularly usually always	**Some** teens **never** get sufficient sleep on weekends **due to** their demanding work schedules. **Many** teens **frequently** fall asleep after midnight **as a result of** late-night texting. **Because** they have to wake up early on school days, **nearly all** teens **usually** prefer to sleep late on weekends.

 USE PRECISE LANGUAGE

Rewrite each simple sentence as a complex sentence, using the reason, quantity, and frequency words in parentheses.

Simple Sentence: Students have trouble completing homework assignments.

Complex Sentence: **As a result of** after-school activities, **some** students **regularly** have trouble completing homework assignments.

1. Punishing cyberbullies is challenging for schools. (*because, usually, nearly all*)

   _____

   _____

2. Junk food bans do not teach teens how to make healthy choices. (*since, never, many*)

   _____

   _____

3. Teens who play video games get into more fights. (*as a result, many, often*)

   _____

   _____

Add a reason, quantity, and frequency to each simple sentence using the chart above.

4. Graffiti can lead to violence.

   _____

   _____

5. Tagging hurts business and property owners.

   _____

   _____

6. Artists express themselves through graffiti.

   _____

   _____

Write a Justification

Prompt | Is graffiti vandalism or art? Write a justification that states and supports your claim.

✏️ WRITE A PARAGRAPH

Use the frame to write your topic sentence, detail sentences, and concluding sentence.

A

The article _____
(title)

and my own relevant experiences as a _____
(relevant personal connection)

_____ lead me to conclude that _____
(your claim)

_____

_____

B

A significant reason is that _____
(reason that supports your claim)

_____

_____

(Transition introducing evidence)

(evidence from the article or your experience)

_____

_____

(Transition introducing a reason)

(reason that supports your claim)

_____

_____

For example, _____
(evidence from the article or your experience)

_____

_____

An equally important point is that _____
(reason that supports your claim)

_____

_____

C

Therefore, I _____ that _____
(verb to agree or disagree)   (restate your claim)

_____

_____

Rate Your Justification

 ASSESS YOUR DRAFT

Rate your justification. Then have a partner rate it.

Scoring Guide	
1	Insufficient
2	Developing
3	Sufficient
4	Exemplary

1. Does the topic sentence clearly state your claim?	Self	1	2	3	4
	Partner	1	2	3	4
2. Did you include strong reasons and evidence to support your claim?	Self	1	2	3	4
	Partner	1	2	3	4
3. Did you include precise topic words?	Self	1	2	3	4
	Partner	1	2	3	4
4. Did you use correct present- and past-tense verbs?	Self	1	2	3	4
	Partner	1	2	3	4
5. Did you use strong verbs to state and restate your claim?	Self	1	2	3	4
	Partner	1	2	3	4
6. Did you include transitions to introduce reasons and evidence?	Self	1	2	3	4
	Partner	1	2	3	4
7. Did you include complex sentences showing cause-effect and opinion?	Self	1	2	3	4
	Partner	1	2	3	4
8. Did you include precise words to specify quantity and frequency?	Self	1	2	3	4
	Partner	1	2	3	4

 REFLECT & REVISE

Record specific priorities and suggestions to help you and your partner revise.

(Partner) Positive Feedback: You did an effective job of (organizing/including/stating)

_____

_____

(Partner) Suggestion: Your justification would be stronger if you _____

_____

_____

(Self) Priority 1: I will revise my justification so that it _____

_____

_____

(Self) Priority 2: I also need to _____

_____

CHECK & EDIT

Use this checklist to proofread and edit your justification.

☐ Is each sentence complete?

☐ Did you use present- and past-tense verbs correctly?

☐ Did you use commas appropriately in complex sentences?

☐ Are all words spelled correctly?

30-Second Speech

IDENTIFY TOPIC
Choose one of the questions below to address in a 30-second speech.

☐ How should our school address cyberbullying?

☐ Should our community encourage or discourage graffiti?

BRAINSTORM IDEAS
Write your claim and two reasons that support it.

My Claim: _____

_____

Reason 1: _____

_____

Reason 2: _____

_____

SYNTHESIZE IDEAS
Take notes on evidence from the text or your experience that supports your claim.

Evidence 1: _____

_____

Evidence 2: _____

_____

WRITE A SPEECH
Write a 30-second speech that states your claim and includes reasons and evidence.

Based on my experiences, I contend that _____

_____

One reason is that _____

_____

Secondly, _____

_____

For example, _____

_____

_____

Therefore, I _____ that _____

_____

_____

Present & Rate Your Speech

Maintaining Eye Contact

Eye contact is when you look at members of the audience. If you are reading a speech, make sure you look up every few seconds. Eye contact helps you look confident and engage your listeners.

PRESENT YOUR SPEECH

Present your speech to the small group. Make sure to maintain eye contact.

TAKE NOTES

Listen attentively to your classmates.
Take notes and write if you agree or disagree.

Language to AFFIRM & CLARIFY
I hadn't thought of that.
One question I have is _____.

Classmate's Name	Idea	Agree/Disagree

ASSESS YOUR SPEECH

Use the Scoring Guide to rate your speech.

Scoring Guide			
1	Insufficient	3	Sufficient
2	Developing	4	Exemplary

	1	2	3	4
1. Did your topic sentence clearly state your claim?	1	2	3	4
2. Did you include strong reasons and evidence to support your speech?	1	2	3	4
3. Did you include precise topic words?	1	2	3	4
4. Did you use a public voice (adequate volume and appropriate pace)?	1	2	3	4
5. Did you maintain eye contact?	1	2	3	4

REFLECT

Think of two ways you can improve for your next speech.

Priority 1: I can improve my next speech by _____

_____

_____

Priority 2: When I present my next speech, I will focus on _____

_____

_____

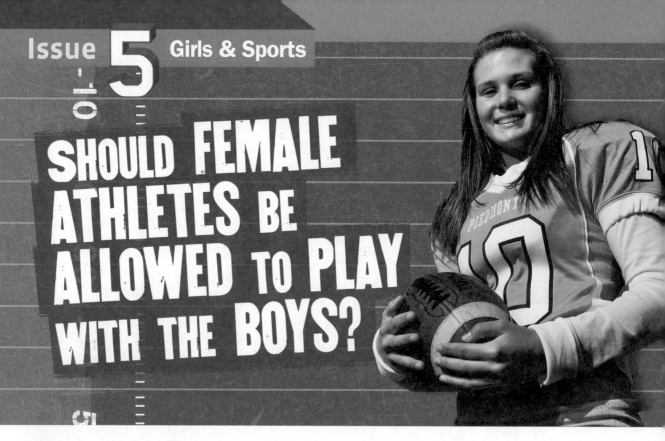

SHOULD FEMALE ATHLETES BE ALLOWED TO PLAY WITH THE BOYS?

 BUILD KNOWLEDGE

Read and respond to the Data File (*Issues*, p. 28).

 BRAINSTORM IDEAS

List sports or physical activities that are traditionally for girls, boys, or both.

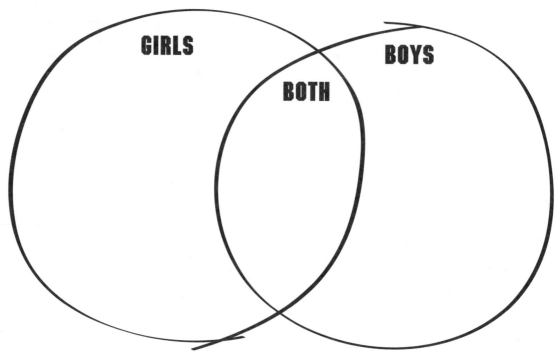

GIRLS   BOYS

BOTH

 PRESENT IDEAS

Use the frames to share ideas with your small group.

• One traditional (girls'/boys') sport is _____.

• A physical fitness activity that many (girls/boys) participate in is _____.

• A sport commonly played by both boys and girls is _____.

Words to Know

 BUILD WORD KNOWLEDGE

Rate your word knowledge. Then complete the chart for each topic-related word.

	① Don't Know	② Recognize	③ Familiar	④ Know

Word to Know	Meaning	Example
aggressive *adjective* ① ② ③ ④	powerful and _____ _____ _____	The basketball players became more **aggressive** when _____ _____
athletic *adjective* ① ② ③ ④	able to _____ _____; related to sports	My sister proved that she is **athletic** when she _____ _____ _____
biased *adjective* ① ② ③ ④	favoring _____ _____ _____ in an unfair way	The referee seems **biased** against our team because he _____ _____ _____
compete *verb* ① ② ③ ④	to try to do _____ _____ at a task, game, or contest	I often **compete** with _____ to see who can _____ _____
contact sport *noun* ① ② ③ ④	a game in which players often _____ _____ _____	Because _____ is a **contact sport**, players protect themselves with _____
discrimination *noun* ① ② ③ ④	the practice of treating people _____ _____ _____	Only letting certain students try out for the _____ _____ would be **discrimination**.
gender *noun* ① ② ③ ④	the sex of a person or animal; _____ _____	Commonly, girls and boys _____ _____ based on their **gender**.
inequality *noun* ① ② ③ ④	an _____ _____ in which some groups have _____ than others	One **inequality** that women may experience is _____ _____ than men.

Academic Discussion

SHOULD GIRLS BE ALLOWED TO COMPETE ON BOYS' SPORTS TEAMS?

 BRAINSTORM IDEAS

Briefly record at least two ideas.

Agree	Disagree

 ANALYZE WORDS

Complete the chart with precise adjectives to discuss and write about the issue.

Everyday	Precise
strong	muscular,
tough	aggressive,
play	compete,

✏️ **MAKE A CLAIM**

Rewrite two ideas using the frames and precise words.

1. **Frame:** In my opinion, girls (should/should not) be allowed to compete on boys' sports teams because they _____ (**present-tense verb:** have, are, can)

   Response: _____

   _____

2. **Frame:** From my perspective, girls (should/should not) be permitted to participate on boys' sports teams due to _____ (**noun phrase:** their athletic ability, the discomfort)

   Response: _____

   _____

 COLLABORATE

Listen attentively, restate, and record your partner's idea.

Classmate's Name	Idea

Language to RESTATE

So your perspective is that _____.

Yes, that's correct.

No, not exactly. What I meant was _____.

Ten-Minute Paper

PRESENT IDEAS

Listen attentively, compare ideas, and take notes.
Then write whether you agree or disagree.

Language to COMPARE IDEAS
I completely (agree/disagree) with _____ 's perspective.

Classmate's Name	Idea	Agree/Disagree

ELABORATE IN WRITING

Work with the teacher to write a ten-minute paper.

From my perspective, girls should be permitted to participate on boys' sports teams

due to their athletic ability. For example, many girls are equally

_____ and _____

As a result, the number of girls competing in high school sports is

_____

_____

_____

_____

Work with a partner to write a ten-minute paper.

From my perspective, girls _____ be permitted to participate on

boys' teams due to _____

_____

_____

For example, _____

_____

_____

As a result, _____

_____

_____

_____

Words to Go

 BUILD WORD KNOWLEDGE

Complete the meanings and examples for this high-utility word.

Word to Go	Meanings	Examples
debate de·bate *noun* de·bate *verb*	a _____ in which people express different opinions; to _____ something when you are trying to make a decision or find a solution	Teens might want to have a **debate** with their family about _____ _____ _____ My friends and I might **debate** which _____ is the most deserving of the _____ _____ award.

 DISCUSS & WRITE EXAMPLES

Discuss your response with a partner. Then complete the sentence in writing.

I would be interested in a **debate** about _____

because _____

Write your response and read it aloud to a partner.

Before we decided _____

we _____ the options.

 BUILD WORD KNOWLEDGE

Complete the meanings and examples for this high-utility word.

Word to Go	Meanings	Examples
opponent op·po·nent *noun*	someone you try to _____ ; someone who _____ with a plan or idea	The runner will face _____ **opponents** in the championship race. While supporters want to raise the driving age, **opponents** argue that _____ _____

 DISCUSS & WRITE EXAMPLES

Discuss your response with a partner. Then complete the sentence in writing.

A school policy that I am an **opponent** of is _____

because _____

Write your response and read it aloud to a partner.

_____ of cell phone bans in schools say that _____

_____

Language to Summarize

📖 BUILD FLUENCY
Read the article introduction and Section 1 (*Issues*, pp. 29–30).

💬 ASK & ANSWER QUESTIONS
Take turns asking and answering questions with a partner.

Q: What is this section of the article **mainly about**?

A: This section of the article is **mainly about** _____.

Q: What are the most **essential details** in this section?

A: One **essential detail** in this section is _____.

A: Another **essential detail** in this section is _____.

Section Shrink

✏️ SUMMARIZE
Complete the topic and important details for Section 1. Then "shrink" the section by writing a summary in 35 or fewer words.

Topic (Who?/What?):   the strength of female athletes

Important Details:
- Opponents claim that girls are _____

_____

- Supporters respond that there is more variation within each
_____ than between them.

- Female athletes are _____ because sports
improve their strength and _____

Partner Summary: Opponents claim that girls are not _____
enough to compete in boys' sports, but others respond that

_____

_____

_____

Word Count: _____

Class Summary: _____

_____

_____

_____

_____

Word Count: _____

Words to Go

 BUILD WORD KNOWLEDGE

Complete the meaning and examples for this high-utility word.

Word to Go	Meaning	Examples
capable ca· pa·ble *adjective*	having the _____ to do something	Most dogs are **capable** of _____ A high school graduate should be **capable** enough to _____ _____

 DISCUSS & WRITE EXAMPLES

Discuss your response with a partner. Then complete the sentence in writing.

With enough practice, I could be **capable** of _____

_____

Write your response and read it aloud to a partner.

A computer is not _____ of _____

_____

 BUILD WORD KNOWLEDGE

Complete the meaning and examples for this high-utility word.

Word to Go	Meaning	Examples
concern con·cern *noun*	a feeling of _____ about something	Most parents share **concerns** about their children's _____ My biggest concern today is _____

 DISCUSS & WRITE EXAMPLES

Discuss your response with a partner. Then complete the sentence in writing.

Many people in my community have **concerns** about _____

_____

Write your response and read it aloud to a partner.

I (do/do not) have _____ about my grades this semester because

_____

_____

Language to Summarize

BUILD FLUENCY
Read Section 2 of the article (*Issues*, pp. 30–32).

ASK & ANSWER QUESTIONS
Take turns asking and answering questions with a partner.

Q: What does this section of the article **focus on**?

A: This section of the article **focuses on** _____.

Q: What are the most **significant details** in this section?

A: One **significant detail** in this section is _____.

A: Another **significant detail** in this section is _____.

Section Shrink

SUMMARIZE
Complete the topic and important details for Section 2. Then "shrink" the section by writing a summary in 35 or fewer words.

Topic (Who?/What?):   the effect of Title IX on _____

Important Details: • Some _____ have been eliminated.

   • Supporters respond that boys still have better _____

   _____

   • Some boy athletes declare that _____

   _____

   • _____

   _____

Partner Summary: Title IX opponents claim that _____

   _____

   but supporters respond that _____

   _____

Word Count: _____

Class Summary: _____

   _____

   _____

   _____

Word Count: _____

Words to Go

 BUILD WORD KNOWLEDGE

Complete the meaning and examples for this high-utility word.

Word to Go	Meaning	Examples
argue ar•gue *verb*	to state an _____	Supporters of a later school start time argue that _____ _____ The class president **argued** that students should be allowed to _____ _____

DISCUSS EXAMPLES

Discuss your response with a partner. Then complete the sentence in writing.

I would **argue** that athletes who use steroids _____

based upon _____

_____

 BUILD WORD KNOWLEDGE

Complete the meaning and examples for this high-utility word.

Word to Go	Meaning	Examples
argument ar•gu•ment *noun*	the statement of an _____	When you _____ having strong **arguments** is important. An **argument** against texting and driving is that _____ _____

DISCUSS EXAMPLES

Discuss your response with a partner. Then complete the sentence in writing.

One **argument** against raising the driving age is that _____

_____

WRITE EXAMPLES

Write your response and read it aloud to a partner.

An _____ for going to college is that it will _____

In a debate over school uniforms, I would _____ that

_____

Quote Quest

BUILD FLUENCY
Read Section 3 of the article (*Issues*, pp. 32–33).

ANALYZE TEXT
Record a quote that either supports or contradicts your position. Then use a frame to paraphrase the quote.

Quote: _____

_____

_____

_____

Paraphrase: _____

_____

_____

> **Language to PARAPHRASE**
>
> This quote clarifies that _____.
>
> In this quote, the author states _____.

SYNTHESIZE IDEAS
Write a topic sentence and two supporting sentences to respond to the quote.

Topic Sentence: I (agree/disagree) with the statement that _____.

_____

_____

_____

Supporting Sentence 1: (For example/Drawing from my own experience), _____.

_____

_____

_____

Supporting Sentence 2: (As a result/Consequently), _____.

_____

_____

_____

COLLABORATE
Listen attentively as each member of your group reads a quote aloud. Then take turns using a frame to respond.

> **Language to RESPOND**
>
> This statement caught my attention.
>
> This quote interested me as well.
>
> This statement reminded me of my experience as a _____.
>
> This statement concerned me.

Student Writing Model

Academic Writing Type

A **formal written summary** provides an objective overview of the topic and important details from an informational text. The writer credits the author, but writes in primarily his or her own words, without including personal opinions.

A. The **topic sentence** includes the text type, title, author, and topic.

B. **Detail sentences** include the important details from the summarized text.

C. The **concluding sentence** restates the author's conclusion in the writer's own words.

ANALYZE TEXT

Read this student model to analyze the elements of a formal summary.

A   In the article titled "Game On or Game Over?," Oscar Gomez investigates how video games affect teens. First, Gomez reports that teens can become addicted to video games. The author also describes how video games can improve coordination and prepare people for certain professions. In addition, he explains that experts disagree about whether violence in games has significant effects.

B

C   Finally, Gomez concludes that video games can have a strong influence on teens.

MARK & DISCUSS ELEMENTS

Mark the summary elements and use the frames to discuss them with your partner.

1. **Underline the four elements of the topic sentence.** *The topic sentence includes _____.*

2. **Check three important details.** *One important detail in this summary is _____.*

3. **Box three transition words or phrases.** *One transition (word/phrase) is _____.*

4. **Circle five citation verbs.** *One citation verb that the writer uses is _____.*

5. **Star four precise topic words.** *An example of a precise topic word is _____.*

Choose Language for Writing

Prompt | Write a formal summary of "Face-Off on the Playing Field."

 IDENTIFY PRECISE WORDS

Review the article to identify precise words and phrases for your summary.

Introduction	Section 1	Section 2	Section 3
• Title IX	• contact sports	• supporters	• society
• discrimination	• physically	• athletic programs	• _____
• success	• self-confident	• _____	• _____
• _____	• _____	• _____	• _____
• _____	• _____	• _____	• _____
• _____	• _____	• _____	• _____

Organize Key Ideas & Details

TAKE NOTES

Record information about the article.

Title: _____

Author: _____

Topic: _____

State the text information to write a topic sentence.

In the article titled (title) _____

(author's full name) _____

(citation verb: explores, examines, discusses) _____

(topic) _____

List three important details from the article in your own words.

1. _____

_____

2. _____

_____

3. _____

_____

Restate the author's conclusion in your own words.

_____

_____

Nouns & Pronouns to Credit an Author

Guidelines to Credit an Author

Topic Sentence: State the author's full name.
1st Important Detail: State the author's last name.
2nd Important Detail: Use the term "author" or "writer."
3rd Important Detail: Use the pronoun "he" or "she."
Concluding Sentence: Use the author's last name.

 IDENTIFY NOUNS & PRONOUNS

Read the summary and circle the nouns and pronouns that credit the author.

> In the blog post titled "Do You Know What Today Is?," Amanda Rykoff discusses the 25th anniversary of National Girls and Women in Sports Day. First, Rykoff argues that more people might identify February 2 as the first day high school football players can commit to a college. The author also describes how the day was celebrated in Washington, D.C., with champion female athletes. In addition, she points out that Title IX has resulted in many improvements for women in sports, with one in three high school girls competing. Finally, Rykoff concludes that we should acknowledge achievements in women's athletics, but continue to strive for complete gender equality.

 TAKE NOTES

Write nouns and pronouns you can use to credit the author in your formal summary.

Summary Sentence	Noun/Pronoun to Credit the Author
Topic Sentence	
1st Detail	
2nd Detail	
3rd Detail	
Concluding Sentence	

Citation Verbs

Noun/Pronoun	Citation Verbs		Summary
(Author's full name)	*explores*	*presents*	(topic)
	investigates	*examines*	
	discusses		
(Author's last name)	*reports*	*notes*	*that/how* (important detail)
The author	*describes*	*clarifies*	
The writer	*explains*	*suggests*	
He/She	*emphasizes*	*questions*	
(Author's last name)	*concludes*		*that* (conclusion)

IDENTIFY CITATION VERBS

Circle the citation verbs in the chart that you plan to use in your summary. Then complete each sentence with an appropriate citation verb.

1. The article _____ whether cheerleading should be considered a sport.

2. The writer _____ how a Connecticut university replaced volleyball with cheerleading.

3. Finally, she _____ that changing the name of cheerleading to "team stunts and gymnastics" would affect whether more people would view the women as athletes.

WRITE KEY DETAILS

Write three sentences about "Face-Off on the Playing Field" using citation verbs.

1. _____   _____
   (noun/pronoun)   (citation verb)

   _____
   (important detail)

   _____

2. _____   _____
   (noun/pronoun)   (citation verb)

   _____
   (important detail)

   _____

3. _____   _____
   (noun/pronoun)   (citation verb)

   _____
   (important detail)

   _____

Write a Summary

Prompt | Write a formal summary of "Face-Off on the Playing Field."

✏ WRITE A PARAGRAPH

Use the frame to write your topic sentence, detail sentences, and concluding sentence.

A

In the article titled _____
(title)

_____ _____
(author's full name)   (citation verb)

_____
(topic)

_____

_____

_____

B

First, _____ _____
(author's last name)   (citation verb)

_____
(important detail)

_____

_____

_____

The (author/writer) _____ also _____
(citation verb)

_____
(important detail)

_____

_____

_____

In addition, (he/she) _____ _____
(citation verb)

_____
(important detail)

_____

_____

_____

C

Finally, _____ concludes that _____
(author's last name)

_____
(restate author's conclusion)

_____

_____

_____

Rate Your Summary

 ASSESS YOUR DRAFT

Rate your formal summary. Then have a partner rate it.

		1	2	3	4
1. Does the topic sentence include the title, author, and topic?	Self	1	2	3	4
	Partner	1	2	3	4
2. Did you discuss the most important details in your own words?	Self	1	2	3	4
	Partner	1	2	3	4
3. Did you use present-tense citation verbs to credit the author?	Self	1	2	3	4
	Partner	1	2	3	4
4. Did you include precise topic words?	Self	1	2	3	4
	Partner	1	2	3	4
5. Did you include a variety of sentences (simple, compound, complex)?	Self	1	2	3	4
	Partner	1	2	3	4

 REFLECT & REVISE

Record specific priorities and suggestions to help you and your partner revise.

(Partner) Positive Feedback: I appreciate how you (used/included) _____.

_____

_____

(Partner) Suggestion: As you revise your summary, focus on _____

_____

_____

(Self) Priority 1: My summary paragraph needs _____

_____

_____

(Self) Priority 2: I plan to improve my summary by _____

_____

_____

✓ **CHECK & EDIT**

Use this checklist to proofread and edit your summary.

☐ Is the title of the article capitalized and in quotations?

☐ Do present-tense verbs that summarize end in –s?

☐ Is each sentence complete?

☐ Are all words spelled correctly?

Is animal testing an experiment in cruelty?

 BUILD KNOWLEDGE

Read and respond to the Data File (*Issues,* p. 34).

BRAINSTORM IDEAS

Complete a concept map about how humans use animals.

scientific research

WAYS THAT HUMANS USE ANIMALS

 PRESENT IDEAS

Use the frames to share ideas with your small group.

• One way that humans use animals is (for/as) _____.

• People also use animals (for/as) _____, such as _____.

Words to Know

 BUILD WORD KNOWLEDGE

Rate your word knowledge. Then complete the chart for each topic-related word

① Don't Know	② Recognize	③ Familiar	④ Know

Word to Know	Meaning	Example
contribute *verb* ① ② ③ ④	to _____ _____ happen	Sean is confident that his _____ _____ will **contribute** to the success of _____ _____
controversy *noun* ① ② ③ ④	a _____ _____ among many people	A big **controversy** at school right now is _____ _____
cruel *adjective* ① ② ③ ④	purposely causing _____ _____	_____ _____ is not only **cruel**, but also doesn't usually solve the problem.
experiment *noun* ① ② ③ ④	a _____ _____ to try out an _____ or to see the _____ of something	I finally agreed with my mother after she told me about an **experiment** proving that _____ _____ _____
progress *noun* ① ② ③ ④	a slow _____ _____	Due to **progress** in technology, _____ _____ _____
replace *verb* ① ② ③ ④	to _____ something or someone _____ _____	A new _____ _____ at school **replaced** the previous one.
similar *adjective* ① ② ③ ④	almost _____ _____	My _____ is **similar** to yours because _____ _____ _____
toxic *adjective* ① ② ③ ④	containing _____	Because of _____ , many people in the world have to deal with **toxic** _____ _____

Academic Discussion

Should scientists be able to use animals for research?

 BRAINSTORM IDEAS

Briefly record at least two ideas.

Agree	Disagree

 ANALYZE WORDS

Complete the chart with precise words to discuss and write about the issue.

Everyday	Precise
harmful	poisonous,
important	essential,
help	assist,

 MAKE A CLAIM

Rewrite two ideas using the frames and precise words.

1. **Frame:** From my perspective, scientists (should/should not) be able to use animals for research due to _____ (**noun phrase:** the medical benefits, the suffering)

   Response: _____

   _____

2. **Frame:** In my opinion, scientists (should/should not) be permitted to use animals for research if they _____ (**present-tense verb:** practice, have, ensure)

   Response: _____

   _____

 COLLABORATE

Listen attentively, restate, and record your partner's idea.

Classmate's Name	Idea

Language to RESTATE

So your (opinion/ perspective) is that _____.

Yes, that's correct.

No, not exactly. What I meant was _____.

Ten-Minute Paper

 PRESENT IDEAS

Listen attentively, compare ideas, and take notes. Then write whether you agree or disagree.

Language to COMPARE IDEAS

I (agree/disagree) with _____'s (opinion/perspective).

Classmate's Name	Idea	Agree/Disagree

 ELABORATE IN WRITING

Work with the teacher to write a ten-minute paper.

> In my opinion, scientists should be permitted to use animals for research if they ensure that the animals die for an important cause. For example, animals are often used in _____ to find out if a treatment for cancer is _____ for humans. As a result, their deaths
>
> _____
> _____
> _____
> _____

Work with a partner to write a ten-minute paper.

> In my opinion, scientists _____ be permitted to use animals for research if they _____
> _____
> _____
>
> For example, _____
> _____
> _____
>
> As a result, _____
> _____
> _____
> _____

Words to Go

 BUILD WORD KNOWLEDGE

Complete the meaning and examples for this high-utility word.

Word to Go	Meaning	Examples
primary pri•mar•y *adjective*	main or most _____	A **primary** cause of _____ _____ is _____ My principal says that _____ _____ (is/are) of **primary** importance.

DISCUSS & WRITE EXAMPLES

Discuss your response with a partner. Then complete the sentence in writing.

My **primary** goal at school is to _____

so that _____

Write your response and read it aloud to a partner.

I think the _____ concern of teens who are involved in many

activities is _____

BUILD WORD KNOWLEDGE

Complete the meanings and examples for this high-utility word.

Word to Go	Meanings	Examples
research re•search *noun* re•search *verb*	careful _____ and _____ to discover new facts or test ideas; to _____ a subject in detail	**Research** about _____ _____ might help teens who _____ _____ Someday, I would like to **research** _____ _____ _____

DISCUSS & WRITE EXAMPLES

Discuss your response with a partner. Then complete the sentence in writing.

For a report last year, I **researched** _____

_____

Write your response and read it aloud to a partner.

Scientific _____ can improve people's lives by _____

_____

Language to Summarize

BUILD FLUENCY

Read the article introduction and Section 1 (*Issues*, pp. 35–37).

ASK & ANSWER QUESTIONS

Take turns asking and answering questions with a partner.

Q: What is this section of the article **mainly about?**

A: This section of the article is **mainly about** _____.

Q: What are the **most essential details** in this section?

A: One **essential detail** in this section is _____.

A: Another **essential detail** in this section is _____.

Section Shrink

SUMMARIZE

Complete the topic and important details for Section 1. Then "shrink" the section by writing a summary in 35 or fewer words.

Topic (Who?/What?):   the benefits of testing on animals

Important Details: • Almost all doctors support animal research because _____

_____

• Animals make good research subjects due to _____

_____

• Supporters of animal research think experimenting on animals

   is more _____ than experimenting on people.

Partner Summary: Doctors and other proponents support using animals in

_____ because _____

_____

_____

Word Count: _____

Class Summary: _____

_____

_____

_____

_____

Word Count: _____

Words to Go

 BUILD WORD KNOWLEDGE

Complete the meaning and examples for this high-utility word.

Word to Go	Meaning	Examples
regulation reg·u·la·tion *noun*	an official _____ or order	_____ _____ is one regulation we have to follow at _____ Regulations are useful ways to make sure _____ _____

 DISCUSS & WRITE EXAMPLES

Discuss your response with a partner. Then complete the sentence in writing.

A **regulation** at school requires students to _____

_____

Write your response and read it aloud to a partner.

When riding a bike, one of the most important safety _____ is

_____

 BUILD WORD KNOWLEDGE

Complete the meaning and examples for this high-utility word.

Word to Go	Meaning	Examples
rely re·ly *verb*	to _____ someone or something	My parents **rely** on me to _____ _____ I don't want to have to **rely** on _____ _____ because _____ _____

 DISCUSS & WRITE EXAMPLES

Discuss your response with a partner. Then complete the sentence in writing.

I proved that I could be **relied** on when I _____

_____

Write your response and read it aloud to a partner.

I am _____ on _____

_____ to improve my grades this year.

Language to Summarize

BUILD FLUENCY

Read Section 2 of the article (*Issues*, pp. 37–38).

ASK & ANSWER QUESTIONS

Take turns asking and answering questions with a partner.

Q: What does this section of the article **focus on**?

A: This section of the article **focuses on** _____.

Q: What are the **most significant details** in this section?

A: One **significant detail** in this section is _____.

A: Another **significant detail** in this section is _____.

Section Shrink

SUMMARIZE

Complete the topic and important details for Section 2. Then "shrink" the section by writing a summary in 35 or fewer words.

Topic (Who?/What?): how research affects _____

Important Details: • Test animals have been seen _____

_____

• The Humane Society website describes _____

_____

• _____

_____

Partner Summary: Critics of animal testing _____

_____

to support their claim that _____

_____

_____

Word Count: _____

Class Summary: _____

_____

_____

_____

Word Count: _____

Words to Go

 BUILD WORD KNOWLEDGE

Complete the meanings and examples for this high-utility word.

Word to Go	Meanings	Examples
alternative al·ter·na·tive *adjective* al·ter·na·tive *noun*	offering a _____ way, plan, or idea as a choice; something chosen _____ of something else	When the first attempt didn't work, _____ used alternative methods to _____ _____ I know my family considered every alternative before _____

 DISCUSS & WRITE EXAMPLES

Discuss your response with a partner. Then complete the sentence in writing.

An energy source that is an **alternative** to oil is _____

_____

Write your response and read it aloud to a partner.

My friend thought he saw a UFO, but an _____ explanation is

that it was _____

 BUILD WORD KNOWLEDGE

Complete the meaning and examples for this high-utility word.

Word to Go	Meaning	Examples
ensure en·sure *verb*	to make _____ that something will happen properly	Many parents _____ _____ to **ensure** that homework gets done. _____ are meant to **ensure** the safety of _____

 DISCUSS & WRITE EXAMPLES

Discuss your response with a partner. Then complete the sentence in writing.

I **ensured** that I would be ready for the math test last week by _____

_____

Write your response and read it aloud to a partner.

People should change their email passwords regularly to _____

the _____

Quote Quest

BUILD FLUENCY
Read Section 3 of the article (*Issues*, pp. 38–39).

ANALYZE TEXT
Record a quote that supports or contradicts your
position. Then use a frame to paraphrase the quote.

Language to PARAPHRASE
In this quote, the author states _____.
In other words, _____.

Quote: _____

_____

_____

_____

Paraphrase: _____

_____

_____

SYNTHESIZE IDEAS
Write a topic sentence and two supporting sentences to respond to the quote.

Topic Sentence: I (agree/disagree) with the statement that _____.

_____

_____

_____

Supporting Sentence 1: (For example,/Drawing from my own experience,) _____.

_____

_____

_____

Supporting Sentence 2: (As a result,/Consequently,) _____.

_____

_____

_____

COLLABORATE
Listen attentively as each member of your
group reads a quote aloud. Then take turns
using a frame to respond.

Language to RESPOND
This statement caught my attention.
I found this quote interesting.
This statement alarmed me.
This statement concerned me as a _____.

Student Writing Model

Academic Writing Type

A **formal written summary** provides an objective overview of the topic and important details from an informational text. The writer credits the author, but writes in primarily his or her own words, without including personal opinions.

A. The **topic sentence** includes the text type, title, author, and topic.
B. **Detail sentences** include the important details from the summarized text.
C. The **concluding sentence** restates the author's conclusion in the writer's own words.

ANALYZE TEXT

Read this student model to analyze the elements of a formal summary.

A
    In the article titled "Food Fight," Dora Rodriguez explores the issue of whether junk food should be sold in schools. First,

B
Rodriguez points out that many people believe offering junk food sends a message that a diet lacking in nutrition is acceptable, even though it causes obesity and other health problems. The author also explains that those opposed to a ban say the snacks provide energy for students who spend long days at school and the extra money benefits schools. In addition, she reports that some proponents believe the government should address the problem while others think families and teens themselves are responsible. Finally, Rodriguez concludes that the question of

C
whether schools should ban junk food or leave teens to make their own choices is still open to debate.

MARK & DISCUSS ELEMENTS

Mark the summary elements and use the frames to discuss them with your partner.

1. **Underline the four elements of the topic sentence.** *The topic sentence includes _____.*
2. **Check three important details.** *One important detail in this summary is _____.*
3. **Draw a box around four transitions.** *One transition (word/phrase) is _____.*
4. **Circle five citation verbs.** *One citation verb that the writer uses is _____.*
5. **Star four precise topic words.** *An example of a precise topic word is _____.*

Choose Language for Writing

Prompt | Write a formal summary of "Animal Testing: Science or Shame?"

IDENTIFY PRECISE WORDS
Review the article to identify precise words and phrases for your summary.

Introduction	Section 1	Section 2	Section 3
• scientists	• supporters	• substance	• limited
• critics	• medical research	• animal rights	• _____
• animal testing	• humane	• _____	• _____
• _____	• _____	• _____	• _____
• _____	• _____	• _____	• _____
• _____	• _____	• _____	

Organize Key Ideas & Details

TAKE NOTES
Record information about the article

Title: _____

Author: _____

Topic: _____

State the text information to write a topic sentence.

In the article titled (title) _____

(author's full name) _____

(verb: explores, examines, discusses) _____

(topic) _____

List three important details from the article in your own words.

1. _____

_____

2. _____

_____

3. _____

_____

Restate the author's conclusion in your own words.

_____

_____

Simple Present-Tense Verbs

Guidelines for Using Simple Present-Tense Verbs

Writers use **simple present-tense verbs** in formal summaries to cite an author or text. For third-person singular pronouns (*he, she,* or *it*), **simple present-tense verbs** end in *-s* or *-es*.

Topic Sentence: State the topic.

The article explores . . .   The reporter discusses . . .   DeShawn Harris investigates . . .

Important Details: Summarize details.

She reports . . .   The writer describes . . .   The article explains . . .

Concluding Sentence: Restate the conclusion.

Harris concludes . . .   The author sums up . . .   DeShawn Harris ends . . .

 IDENTIFY PRESENT-TENSE VERBS

Read the summary and circle the third-person singular, present-tense verbs.

> In the news article titled "Cruelty-Free Dog Food?," Melinda Lee explores the possibility of feeding dogs a strictly vegan diet. First, Lee explains that most veterinarians agree that dogs do not require meat in their diets. The author also reports that a diet without animal by-products reduces the allergies that affect many dogs. In addition, she emphasizes that one of the oldest dogs on record—Bramble, a collie from Britain—feasts only on vegan food. Finally, Lee concludes that a vegan or vegetarian diet not only benefits dogs, but also helps all the animals that no longer have to die to feed pets.

 WRITE PRESENT-TENSE VERBS

Complete each sentence with the third-person singular form of the verb in parentheses.

1. Grover Banks _____ animal testing labs once a month to monitor them. (*visit*)

2. He _____ experiments and _____ any inhumane treatment. (*observe, report*)

3. The agency he works for _____ to end animal testing, but for now it _____ that animals are treated humanely. (*hope, ensure*)

4. To unwind from the stresses of his job, Banks _____ his free time playing with his three dogs. (*spend*)

Transitions to Organize Details

Organization	Transitions		Examples
first detail	*First,*	*To begin with,*	**First,** the author states that many doctors support animal research.
additional details	*The article also* *In addition,* *Moreover,*	*The author also* *Additionally,* *Furthermore,*	**The article also** describes the effect of testing cosmetics on rabbits. **Furthermore,** he points out that test animals are similar to humans.
last detail	*Finally,*	*Lastly,*	**Finally,** the author concludes that too many animals die in science labs.

IDENTIFY TRANSITIONS

Circle the transitions in the chart that you plan to use in your summary. Then complete the model summary with appropriate transition.

_____ the author explains that many people oppose using animals for clothing. _____ he describes how animals are used for fur, leather, silk, and wool. _____ reports that some people only oppose killing animals for clothing while others oppose any use of animals. _____ the author concludes that many people remain passionate about the issue.

WRITE IMPORTANT DETAILS

Write three sentences about "Animal Testing: Science or Shame?" using transitions.

1. _____ _____
   (Transition)   (noun/pronoun)

   _____ that _____
   (citation verb)   (important detail)

   _____

   _____

2. _____ _____
   (Transition)   (noun/pronoun)

   _____ that _____
   (citation verb)   (important detail)

   _____

   _____

3. _____ _____
   (Transition)   (noun/pronoun)

   _____ that _____
   (citation verb)   (important detail)

   _____

   _____

Write a Summary

Prompt | Write a formal summary of "Animal Testing: Science or Shame?"

✏️ WRITE A PARAGRAPH

Use the frame to write your topic sentence, detail sentences, and concluding sentence.

A

In the article titled _____
(title)

_____ _____
(author's full name)   (citation verb)

_____
(topic)

_____

_____

_____

B

_____ _____
(Transition)   (author's last name)

_____ _____
(citation verb)   (important detail)

_____

_____

_____

The (author/writer) _____ also _____
                                              (citation verb)

_____
(important detail)

_____

_____

_____ (he/she) _____ _____
(Transition)   (citation verb)

_____
(important detail)

_____

_____

C

_____ _____
(Transition)   (author's last name)

concludes that _____
                 (restate author's conclusion)

_____

_____

_____

Rate Your Summary

Scoring Guide	
1	Insufficient
2	Developing
3	Sufficient
4	Exemplary

ASSESS YOUR DRAFT

Rate your formal summary. Then have a partner rate it.

1. Does the topic sentence include the title, author, and topic?	Self	1	2	3	4
	Partner	1	2	3	4
2. Did you discuss the most important details in your own words?	Self	1	2	3	4
	Partner	1	2	3	4
3. Did you use transitions to sequence and introduce details?	Self	1	2	3	4
	Partner	1	2	3	4
4. Did you use present-tense citation verbs to credit the author?	Self	1	2	3	4
	Partner	1	2	3	4
5. Did you include precise topic words?	Self	1	2	3	4
	Partner	1	2	3	4
6. Did you include a variety of sentences (simple, compound, complex)?	Self	1	2	3	4
	Partner	1	2	3	4

REFLECT & REVISE

Record specific priorities and suggestions to help you and your partner revise.

(Partner) Positive Feedback: I appreciate how you (used/included) _____

_____

_____

(Partner) Suggestion: As you revise your summary, focus on _____

_____

_____

(Self) Priority 1: My summary paragraph needs _____

_____

_____

(Self) Priority 2: I plan to improve my summary by _____

_____

_____

CHECK & EDIT

Use this checklist to proofread and edit your summary.

☐ Did you use a comma after transition words and phrases?

☐ Do present-tense citation verbs end in –s or –es?

☐ Is each sentence complete?

☐ Are all words spelled correctly?

30-Second Speech

IDENTIFY TOPIC

Choose one of the questions below to address in a 30-second speech.

☐ Should our school have more girls' sports teams?

☐ Should our school use animals in science classes?

BRAINSTORM IDEAS

Write your claim and two reasons that support it.

My Claim: _____

_____

Reason 1: _____

_____

Reason 2: _____

_____

SYNTHESIZE IDEAS

Take notes on evidence from the text or your experience that supports your claim.

Evidence 1: _____

_____

Evidence 2: _____

_____

WRITE A SPEECH

Write a 30-second speech that states your claim and includes reasons and evidence.

From my perspective, our school should _____

_____

First of all, _____

_____

_____

Additionally, _____

_____

_____

This is important because _____

_____

_____

For these reasons, I _____ that _____

_____

_____

Present & Rate Your Speech

Speaking at an Appropriate Pace

Pacing is how fast you speak. When you want to emphasize a point, try pausing for a short time afterward to allow your audience to think about what you have said. You can also pause or slow down to avoid fillers such as *um, so,* or *like.*

PRESENT YOUR SPEECH

Present your speech to the small group. Make sure to speak at an appropriate pace.

TAKE NOTES

Listen attentively to your classmates.
Take notes and write if you agree or disagree.

> **Language to AFFIRM & CLARIFY**
> That's an interesting opinion.
> Will you explain _____ again?

Classmate's Name	Idea	Agree/Disagree

ASSESS YOUR SPEECH

Use the Scoring Guide to rate your speech.

Scoring Guide			
1	Insufficient	3	Sufficient
2	Developing	4	Exemplary

	1	2	3	4
1. Did your topic sentence clearly state your claim?	1	2	3	4
2. Did you include strong reasons and evidence to support your speech?	1	2	3	4
3. Did you include precise topic words?	1	2	3	4
4. Did you maintain eye contact?	1	2	3	4
5. Did you speak at an appropriate pace?	1	2	3	4

REFLECT

Think of two ways you can improve for your next speech.

Priority 1: I can improve my next speech by _____

_____

_____

Priority 2: When I present my next speech, I will focus on _____

_____

_____

IS IT TIME TO TRASH PLASTIC BAGS?

 BUILD KNOWLEDGE
Read and respond to the Data File (*Issues*, p. 40).

 BRAINSTORM IDEAS
Complete a concept map about how people use plastic bags.

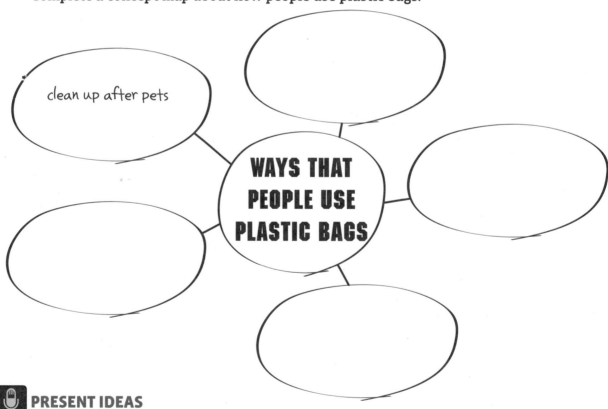

clean up after pets

WAYS THAT PEOPLE USE PLASTIC BAGS

 PRESENT IDEAS
Use the frames to share ideas with your small group.

- One common use for plastic bags is to _____.
- People typically use plastic bags to _____.
- Another way that people use plastic bags is for _____.

Words to Know

 BUILD WORD KNOWLEDGE
Rate your word knowledge. Then complete the chart for each topic-related word.

	① Don't Know	② Recognize	③ Familiar	④ Know

Word to Know	Meaning	Example
disposable *adjective* ① ② ③ ④	designed to be used briefly and _____ _____	**Disposable** towels make _____ _____ _____ easier.
implement *verb* ① ② ③ ④	to begin a plan _____ _____	Once my lab partners and I _____ _____ _____, we were ready to **implement** the experiment.
litter *verb* ① ② ③ ④	to leave _____ lying around	The mayor signed a law making it a crime to **litter** _____ _____
pollution *noun* ① ② ③ ④	harmful materials that _____ _____ the air, water, and soil	One way to cut down on **pollution** is to _____ _____ _____
recycle *verb* ① ② ③ ④	to put used objects through a process so they can be _____ _____	The specially marked bins at school encourage students to **recycle** _____
retailers *noun* ① ② ③ ④	people or businesses that _____ to customers	The most successful **retailers** in my community sell _____ _____ _____
reusable *adjective* ① ② ③ ④	capable of being used _____ _____	Packing lunch in **reusable** containers helps _____ _____
tax *noun* ① ② ③ ④	money paid to _____ _____ for public services, such as education and roads	The politician said the new **tax** would benefit our community by _____ _____

Academic Discussion

SHOULD CITIES OUTLAW PLASTIC BAGS?

 BRAINSTORM IDEAS

Briefly record at least two ideas.

Agree	Disagree

 ANALYZE WORDS

Complete the chart with precise words to discuss and write about the issue.

Everyday	Precise
trash	refuse,
get rid of	outlaw,
useful	convenient,

✏️ **MAKE A CLAIM**

Rewrite two ideas using the frames and precise words.

1. **Frame:** From my perspective, cities (should/should not) prohibit plastic bags because they are _____ **(adjective)** and _____ **(adjective)**.

   Response: _____

   _____

2. **Frame:** Due to _____ **(noun phrase)**, I believe that cities (should/should not) outlaw plastic bags.

   Response: _____

   _____

 COLLABORATE

Listen attentively, restate, and record your partner's idea.

Classmate's Name	Idea

Language to RESTATE

If I understand you correctly, your (opinion/perspective) is that _____.

Yes, that's correct.

No, not quite. What I meant was _____.

Ten-Minute Paper

PRESENT IDEAS

Listen attentively, compare ideas, and take notes.
Then write whether you agree or disagree.

Language to COMPARE IDEAS
My perspective on _____ is similar to _____'s.

Classmate's Name	Idea	Agree/Disagree

ELABORATE IN WRITING

Work with the teacher to write a ten-minute paper.

Due to the convenience of reusable bags, I believe that cities should not outlaw

plastic bags. For example, many people reuse plastic bags to _____

_____

As a result, people have _____

_____

and there is _____

_____

_____

Work with a partner to write a ten-minute paper.

Due to _____,

I believe that cities _____ outlaw plastic bags. For example,

_____

_____

_____

_____

As a result, _____

_____

_____

_____

Words to Go

 BUILD WORD KNOWLEDGE

Complete the meaning and examples for this high-utility word.

Word to Go	Meaning	Examples
environment en·vi·ron·ment *noun*	the _____ _____ in which people, plants, and animals live	I care about the **environment**, so I _____ _____ Residents of the coldest **environments** in the world survive by _____ _____ _____

 DISCUSS & WRITE EXAMPLES

Discuss your response with a partner. Then complete the sentence in writing.

In my opinion, the best place to live is in an **environment** where the climate is

_____

Write your response and read it aloud to a partner.

You can help protect the _____ by _____

_____

BUILD WORD KNOWLEDGE

Complete the meaning and examples for this high-utility word.

Word to Go	Meaning	Examples
legislation leg·is·la·tion *noun*	a _____ or group of _____	Our town has **legislation** that prohibits _____ One important piece of **legislation** the government passed states that _____ _____ _____

DISCUSS & WRITE EXAMPLES

Discuss your response with a partner. Then complete the sentence in writing.

One piece of **legislation** most teens would argue against is _____

_____

Write your response and read it aloud to a partner.

The school board members debated and voted to pass _____

to ban _____

Language to Summarize

BUILD FLUENCY
Read the article introduction and Section 1 (*Issues*, pp. 41–42).

ASK & ANSWER QUESTIONS
Take turns asking and answering questions with a partner.

Q: What does this section of the article **focus on**?

A: This section of the article **focuses on** _____.

Q: What are the **most significant details** in this section?

A: One **significant detail** in this section is _____.

A: Another **significant detail** in this section is _____.

Section Shrink

SUMMARIZE
Complete the topic and important details for Section 1. Then "shrink" the section by writing a summary in 35 or fewer words.

Topic (Who?/What?):   concerns about whether to ban plastic bags

Important Details: • In India, China, and San Francisco, _____

_____

• The plastic from disposable bags kills marine mammals and will

_____

• Opponents of a ban feel _____

_____

Partner Summary: Supporters of legislation against plastic bags _____

_____

and argue that _____

_____ However, opponents _____

_____

Word Count: _____

Class Summary: _____

_____

_____

_____

Word Count: _____

Words to Go

 BUILD WORD KNOWLEDGE

Complete the meaning and examples for this high-utility word.

Word to Go	Meaning	Examples
consumer con·sum·er *noun*	someone who _____ or uses products and services	Stores often try to attract **consumers** by _____ _____ Many teenage **consumers** prefer to _____ _____

💬 **DISCUSS & WRITE EXAMPLES**

Discuss your response with a partner. Then complete the sentence in writing.

Consumers can spend less money if they _____

_____

Write your response and read it aloud to a partner.

As a _____, I appreciate when stores _____

_____

📑 **BUILD WORD KNOWLEDGE**

Complete the meanings and examples for this high-utility word.

Word to Go	Meanings	Examples
resource re·source *noun*	available land, water, and natural energy that can be _____; something used to _____ _____	Oil is one **resource** that people use to _____ The science lab is equipped with many **resources**, such as _____ _____, that will help us learn more effectively.

💬 **DISCUSS & WRITE EXAMPLES**

Discuss your response with a partner. Then complete the sentence in writing.

One use of natural **resources** that threatens the planet is _____

_____

Write your response and read it aloud to a partner.

My father says our family has to find the financial _____ to help

_____

_____

Language to Summarize

BUILD FLUENCY

Read Section 2 of the article (*Issues*, pp. 42–44).

ASK & ANSWER QUESTIONS

Take turns asking and answering questions with a partner.

Q: What is the author's **main point**?

A: The author's **main point** is _____.

Q: What are the **most relevant details** in this section?

A: One **relevant detail** in this section is _____.

A: Another **relevant detail** in this section is _____.

Section Shrink

SUMMARIZE

Complete the topic and important details for Section 2. Then "shrink" the section by writing a summary in 35 or fewer words.

Topic (Who?/What?): the benefits of _____

Important Details: • The American Plastics Council defends _____

_____

• Opponents of a ban also claim _____

_____

• _____

_____

Partner Summary: Those who oppose banning plastic bags _____

_____

_____

and _____

_____

Word Count: _____

Class Summary: _____

_____

_____

_____

_____

Word Count: _____

Words to Go

 BUILD WORD KNOWLEDGE

Complete the meaning and examples for this high-utility word.

Word to Go	Meaning	Examples
occur oc·cur *verb*	to take place or _____	_____ does not **occur** often at our school. My favorite athletic event **occurs** every _____

 DISCUSS & WRITE EXAMPLES

Discuss your response with a partner. Then complete the sentence in writing.

One example of a terrifying event that can **occur** without warning is _____

_____

Write your response and read it aloud to a partner.

Police officers _____

_____ after the accident _____

 BUILD WORD KNOWLEDGE

Complete the meaning and examples for this high-utility word.

Word to Go	Meaning	Examples
relevant rel·e·vant *adjective*	directly _____ an issue or matter	The celebrity's message about _____ is **relevant** to most teens' lives today. Yasmine found the article about girls and sports **relevant** because

 DISCUSS & WRITE EXAMPLES

Discuss your response with a partner. Then complete the sentence in writing.

The debate about whether or not junk food should be banned is not **relevant** at our

school because _____

_____

Write your response and read it aloud to a partner.

During our discussion about whether graffiti should be considered art, I made a

_____ point that _____

_____

Quote Quest

BUILD FLUENCY
Read Section 3 of the article (*Issues*, pp. 44–45).

ANALYZE TEXT
Record a quote that supports or contradicts your position. Then use a frame to paraphrase the quote.

Quote: _____

_____

_____

_____

Paraphrase: _____

_____

_____

> **Language to PARAPHRASE**
>
> In other words, _____.
>
> This quote reinforces the idea that _____.

SYNTHESIZE IDEAS
Write a topic sentence and two supporting sentences to respond to the quote.

Topic Sentence: I (agree/disagree) with the statement that _____.

_____

_____

_____

Supporting Sentence 1: (For example,/Drawing from my own experience,) _____.

_____

_____

_____

Supporting Sentence 2: (As a result,/Consequently,) _____.

_____

_____

_____

COLLABORATE
Listen attentively as each member of your group reads a quote aloud. Then take turns using a frame to respond.

> **Language to RESPOND**
>
> I noticed this quote also.
>
> This statement took me by surprise.
>
> This statement reminded me of _____.
>
> I found this statement concerning.

Student Writing Model

Academic Writing Type

A **summary and response** provides an objective overview of the topic and important details from a text and then presents the writer's position on the issue.

A. The **summary** includes a topic sentence, detail sentences, and a concluding sentence.

B. The **response** includes a transitional sentence, a topic sentence that presents the writer's position, supporting details, and a final statement.

ANALYZE TEXT

Read this student model to analyze the elements of a summary and response.

A

In the article titled "The New Bully at School," Lucas Chen examines arguments about who should punish cyberbullies. Chen begins by describing how two teens felt about cyberbullying. The author continues to discuss how one principal responded. He explains further that very few schools took action due to fear of lawsuits. Chen concludes by suggesting that ultimately teens are responsible for their actions.

B

Whether schools should punish cyberbullies or not is a complex question. After considering the evidence presented in Chen's article and my own experiences, I can fully support schools punishing cyberbullies. I am in favor of schools punishing cyberbullies in part because a bully's behavior can impact the school day. To illustrate, the article reports that the bullies who humiliated the student on Facebook also harassed him on campus. My first-hand experiences as a victim who chose to speak up have also helped me understand why students should be able to attend school without fear. For these reasons, I maintain that schools should punish cyberbullies.

MARK & DISCUSS ELEMENTS

Mark the summary and response elements. Then discuss them with your partner.

1. **Underline the writer's position.** *The writer's position is _____.*

2. **Check three reasons or pieces of evidence that support the writer's position.** *One (reason/piece of evidence) is _____.*

3. **Draw boxes around three transition phrases.** *One transition phrase is _____.*

4. **Circle five citation verbs in the essay.** *One citation verb is _____.*

5. **Star four precise topic words.** *An example of a precise topic word is _____.*

Choose Language for Writing

Prompt Write a summary and response for "Ban It or Bag It?"

IDENTIFY PRECISE WORDS
Review the article to identify and record precise words and phrases for your essay.

Introduction	Section 1	Section 2	Section 3
• account for	• landscapes	• reused	• freedom of choice
• nonrenewable	• ocean-borne	• produce	• _____
• plastics industry	• pro-environment	• _____	• _____
• _____	• _____	• _____	• _____
• _____	• _____	• _____	• _____

Organize Key Ideas & Details

TAKE NOTES
State the text information to write a topic sentence.

Topic Sentence: In the article titled (title) _____

(author's full name) _____

(citation verb) _____ (topic) _____

_____

List three important details from the article in your own words.

1. _____

_____

2. _____

_____

3. _____

_____

Describe your position and write a topic sentence.

Topic Sentence: After considering the evidence presented in (author's last name + 's)

_____ article and my own experiences, I (can/cannot)

_____ fully support (issue) _____

List reasons and evidence from the text or your experience that supports your position.

Reasons: _____

_____

Evidence: _____

_____

_____

Irregular Past-Tense Verbs

Guidelines for Using Irregular Past-Tense Verbs

Use a **past-tense verb** to tell about something that already happened. **Irregular past-tense verbs** do not follow the rule of adding -ed. The past tense of an irregular verb has a different spelling from the present tense of the verb.

Use irregular past-tense verbs to describe past events in a summary and response.

Residents **paid** a 5 cent tax for each plastic bag they used.	pay → paid
I **brought** a reusable bag to the store.	bring → brought
The plastic bags that people **left** on the streets **became** "urban tumbleweeds."	leave → left become → became

 IDENTIFY PAST-TENSE VERBS

Read the response below and circle the irregular past-tense verbs.

Whether the New York City government should force retailers to accept plastic bags for recycling or not is a fascinating question. After considering the evidence presented in Barnard's article and my own experiences, I can fully support the city's legislation to require store owners to accept plastic bags for recycling. I am in favor of having stores recycle the bags in part because the city never gave residents another way to recycle plastic bags. To illustrate, the article points out that many people kept piles of the bags under their sinks and forgot about them. My first-hand experiences as a city resident who saw the problem daily have also helped me understand why plastic bags should not litter city streets and hang in neighborhood trees. For these reasons, I maintain that New York City was right when it made businesses accept some responsibility for recycling plastic bags.

 WRITE PAST-TENSE VERBS

Complete the sentences with the irregular past tense of the verbs in parentheses.

1. Before New York City passed the law, residents never _____ what to do with their plastic bags. (*know*)

2. New Yorkers _____ tired of storing piles of plastic bags in their homes. (*grow*)

3. The law _____ retail stores accept the plastic bags for recycling. (*make*)

4. The solution made sense since the stores _____ out the bags in the first place. (*give*)

5. The city _____ of a solution to a challenging problem. (*think*)

Paraphrasing Text

Guidelines for Paraphrasing Text

Look for an important detail or a statement that supports your position in the text. Then **paraphrase** it by restating the idea using precise synonyms and your own words.

Source Text	Key Words & Phrases → Precise Synonyms		Paraphrasing
On the other side of the issue are members of the plastics industry. They think the bags are just a victim of success.	on the other side of the issue	→	opponents of a plastic bag ban	Opponents of a plastic bag ban claim that disposable bags are simply picked on because of their popularity.
	think	→	believe, claim, assert, maintain	
	the bags	→	plastic bags, disposable bags	
	just	→	simply, only	
	a victim of success	→	picked on because of their popularity	

🔍 IDENTIFY PRECISE SYNONYMS

Read these statements and replace the words in parentheses with precise synonyms.

1. In 2007, San Francisco was the first U.S. city to (*pass legislation*) _____

   to (*ban*) _____ plastic bags.

2. The bags are also much more than just (*an eyesore*) _____.

   For wildlife, they can be (*toxic*) _____.

3. Critics of the ban (*argue*) _____ that (*shoppers*)

   _____ will always need bags to hold their (*shopping items*)

   _____.

✏️ PARAPHRASE IDEAS

Paraphrase the three statements above using your own words and phrasing.

1. The author notes that _____

   _____

   _____

2. To illustrate, the article points out that _____

   _____

   _____

3. In addition, the article states that _____

   _____

   _____

Write a Summary & Response

Prompt | Write a summary and response for "Ban It or Bag It?"

 WRITE AN ESSAY
Use the frame to write a two-paragraph summary and response essay.

A

In the article titled _____
(title)

_____
(Author's full name)

_____ _____
(citation verb)   (noun phrase: arguments about, impacts of)

_____
(topic)

_____ begins by _____
(Author's last name)   (verb: describing, identifying, clarifying)

_____
(important detail)

_____

The author continues to _____
(verb: address, discuss, point out)

_____
(important detail)

_____

(He/She) _____ _____
(citation verb)

further that _____
(important detail)

_____

_____ concludes by _____
(Author's last name)   (verb: emphasizing, suggesting, questioning)

_____
(restate author's conclusion)

B

Whether _____ should _____
(noun)   (verb phrase)

or not is a _____ question. After considering the evidence
(precise adjective: fascinating, provocative, complex)

presented in _____ article and my own experiences, I
(Author's last name + 's)

(can/cannot) _____ fully support _____
(issue)

I am _____ _____
(in favor of/opposed to)   (issue)

in part because _____
(reason that supports your position)

To illustrate, _____
(evidence from the article)

_____

My first-hand experiences as a _____
(noun: high school student, part-time worker, etc.)

have also helped me understand why _____
(reason that supports your position)

_____

For these reasons, I maintain that _____
(your position)

Rate Your Summary & Response

Scoring Guide	
1	Insufficient
2	Developing
3	Sufficient
4	Exemplary

ASSESS YOUR DRAFT

Rate your summary and response. Then have a partner rate it.

1. Does the summary topic sentence include the title, author, and topic?	Self	1	2	3	4
	Partner	1	2	3	4
2. Did you discuss the most important details in your own words?	Self	1	2	3	4
	Partner	1	2	3	4
3. Did you use present-tense citation verbs to introduce the author's points?	Self	1	2	3	4
	Partner	1	2	3	4
4. Did your response clearly present your position?	Self	1	2	3	4
	Partner	1	2	3	4
5. Did your response include strong reasons and evidence?	Self	1	2	3	4
	Partner	1	2	3	4
6. Did you use transitions to sequence and introduce supporting points?	Self	1	2	3	4
	Partner	1	2	3	4
7. Did you include precise topic words?	Self	1	2	3	4
	Partner	1	2	3	4
8. Did you include a variety of sentences (simple, compound, complex)?	Self	1	2	3	4
	Partner	1	2	3	4
9. Did you use correct present- and past-tense verbs in your supporting details?	Self	1	2	3	4
	Partner	1	2	3	4
10. Did you conclude with a strong final statement?	Self	1	2	3	4
	Partner	1	2	3	4

REFLECT & REVISE

Record specific priorities and suggestions to help you and your partner revise.

(Partner) Positive Feedback: I appreciate how you (used/included) _____

_____

(Partner) Suggestion: As you revise your summary and response, focus on

_____

(Self) Priority 1: My summary and response essay needs _____

_____

(Self) Priority 2: I plan to improve my summary and response by _____

_____

CHECK & EDIT

Use this checklist to proofread and edit your summary and response.

☐ Did you use correct punctuation?

☐ Did you use present- and past-tense verbs correctly?

☐ Is each sentence complete?

☐ Are all words spelled correctly?

Should skipping school or failing classes keep teens out of the driver's seat?

BUILD KNOWLEDGE
Read and respond to the Data File (*Issues*, p. 46).

BRAINSTORM IDEAS
Complete a concept map about reasons why a student might need to drive.

```
                          (        )
   (                )         |
  run errands for            |
  family members      +------------------+        (        )
   (                ) | REASONS WHY      |
                      | A STUDENT MIGHT  |
                      | NEED TO DRIVE    |
   (                ) +------------------+        (        )
                          |
                      (        )
```

PRESENT IDEAS
Use the frames to share ideas with your small group.

• (One/Another) reason why a student might need to drive is to _____.

• A student might rely on driving to _____.

Words to Know

BUILD WORD KNOWLEDGE

Rate your word knowledge. Then complete the chart for each topic-related word.

	① Don't Know	② Recognize	③ Familiar	④ Know

Word to Know	Meaning	Example
accountable *adjective* ① ② ③ ④	_____ _____ your actions and the effects they have	As Student Council president, I am **accountable** for _____ _____ _____
attendance *noun* ① ② ③ ④	the act of going to or _____ in class, at a meeting, or at another gathering	Your regular **attendance** at soccer practice is necessary if _____ _____
mandatory *adjective* ① ② ③ ④	describing something that must _____ _____	_____ _____ is **mandatory** for bicyclists.
monitor *verb* ① ② ③ ④	to carefully _____ _____ a person or a situation	To make sure I stay safe, my parents **monitor** _____ _____ _____
motivate *verb* ① ② ③ ④	to make someone want to _____ in order to achieve something	The promise of a new MP3 player might **motivate** me to _____ _____ _____
suspend *verb* ① ② ③ ④	to officially _____ _____ temporarily	My dad asked the phone company to **suspend** my cell phone service because _____ _____
truancy *noun* ① ② ③ ④	the act of purposely _____ _____ from school without permission	Tina's frequent **truancy** caused her to _____ _____ _____
tutoring *noun* ① ② ③ ④	the act of _____ _____ someone	Sean's parents decided that he needs regular **tutoring** to help him _____ _____

Academic Discussion
SHOULD DRIVING PRIVILEGES DEPEND ON SCHOOL ATTENDANCE AND GRADES?

 BRAINSTORM IDEAS
Briefly record at least two ideas.

Agree	Disagree

 ANALYZE WORDS
Complete the chart with precise words to discuss and write about the issue.

Everyday	Precise
take away	revoke,
make someone do something	inspire,
get	attain,

 MAKE A CLAIM
Rewrite two ideas using the frames and precise words.

1. **Frame:** From my point of view, driving privileges (should/should not) depend on school attendance and grades because many teens _____ (**present-tense verb**).

   Response: _____

   _____

2. **Frame:** I would argue that driving privileges (should/should not) depend on school attendance and grades in areas where _____ (**noun phrase**).

   Response: _____

   _____

COLLABORATE
Listen attentively, restate, and record your partner's idea.

Classmate's Name	Idea

Language to RESTATE
If I understand you correctly, your point of view is that _____.
Yes, that's correct.
No, not quite. What I meant was _____.

Ten-Minute Paper

 PRESENT IDEAS
Listen attentively, compare ideas, and take notes.
Then write whether you agree or disagree.

Classmate's Name	Idea	Agree/Disagree

 ELABORATE IN WRITING
Work with the teacher to write a ten-minute paper.

I would argue that driving privileges should depend on school attendance and grades in areas where teens can find alternate ways to get around. For example, many teens can _____
_____
As a result, driving a car is not _____
_____, and teens should _____
to earn the privilege.

Work with a partner to write a ten-minute paper.

I would argue that driving privileges _____
depend on school attendance and grades in areas where _____
_____
_____
For example, _____
_____
_____
As a result, _____
_____
_____
_____

Words to Go

 BUILD WORD KNOWLEDGE

Complete the meaning and examples for this high-utility word.

Word to Go	Meaning	Examples
consequence con·se·quence *noun*	something that _____ because of an action	One **consequence** of not completing my homework is _____ _____ Jason's parents warned that he would face serious **consequences** if he _____

 DISCUSS & WRITE EXAMPLES

Discuss your response with a partner. Then complete the sentence in writing.

The **consequence** of Marisa quitting her part-time job without giving notice was that

_____

Write your response and read it aloud to a partner.

Winning the school competition for _____

has many positive _____ , such as _____

_____

_____

 BUILD WORD KNOWLEDGE

Complete the meaning and examples for this high-utility word.

Word to Go	Meaning	Examples
obtain ob·tain *verb*	to get something using _____	Our soccer team might **obtain** the money we need for new uniforms if we _____ _____ My cousin **obtained** a college degree in _____

 DISCUSS & WRITE EXAMPLES

Discuss your response with a partner. Then complete the sentence in writing.

Obtaining _____

_____ would make me the happiest person in the world!

Write your response and read it aloud to a partner.

If you want to _____ ,

you will have to _____ permission from the principal.

Language to Summarize

BUILD FLUENCY
Read the article introduction and Section 1 (*Issues*, pp. 47–48).

ASK & ANSWER QUESTIONS
Take turns asking and answering questions with a partner.

Q: What does this section of the article **focus on**?

A: This section of the article **focuses on** _____.

Q: What are the most **significant details** in this section?

A: One **significant detail** in this section is _____.

A: Another **significant detail** in this section is _____.

Section Shrink

SUMMARIZE
Complete the topic and important details for Section 1. Then "shrink" the section by writing a summary in 35 or fewer words.

Topic (Who?/What?): opposing views on no-pass, no-drive laws

Important Details:
- No-pass, no-drive laws were created to _____
  _____
- Some people believe the laws _____
  _____
- Critics of the laws argue that they _____
  _____

Partner Summary: Supporters of no-pass, no-drive laws _____
_____

while critics _____
_____
_____

Word Count: _____

Class Summary: _____
_____
_____
_____
_____

Word Count: _____

Words to Go

 BUILD WORD KNOWLEDGE

Complete the meaning and examples for this high-utility word.

Word to Go	Meaning	Examples
require re·quire *verb*	to _____ something by law or rule	Her expensive shopping habits **require** that she _____ _____ The school **requires** all athletes to _____ _____ if they want to play sports.

DISCUSS EXAMPLES

Discuss your response with a partner. Then complete the sentence in writing.

My former teacher **required** students to _____

_____ in order to get a passing grade in her class.

BUILD WORD KNOWLEDGE

Complete the meaning and examples for this high-utility word.

Word to Go	Meaning	Examples
requirement re·quire·ment *noun*	something that _____ _____ by law or rule	Sometimes, it seems as though _____ _____ is a **requirement** for being popular at school. One **requirement** for being in the band is _____ _____

DISCUSS EXAMPLES

Discuss your response with a partner. Then complete the sentence in writing.

Laura was upset to discover that _____

_____ was a **requirement** for

_____

WRITE EXAMPLES

Write your response and read it aloud to a partner.

There are many _____ for attending the school field trip, such as

_____

I agree with the rule that _____ all students to _____

_____

Language to Summarize

BUILD FLUENCY
Read Section 2 of the article (*Issues*, pp. 48–50).

ASK & ANSWER QUESTIONS
Take turns asking and answering questions with a partner.

Q: What is the author's **main point**?

A: The author's **main point** is _____.

Q: What are the **most relevant details** in this section?

A: One **relevant detail** in this section is _____.

A: Another **relevant detail** in this section is _____.

Section Shrink

SUMMARIZE
Complete the topic and important details for Section 2. Then "shrink" the section by writing a summary in 35 or fewer words.

Topic (Who?/What?): the question of whether _____

Important Details:
- South Carolina representative Bill Taylor states that driving

  _____

- Others, like student Stephanie Fehr, express that _____

  _____

- _____

  _____

Partner Summary: Some people, _____

_____

while _____

_____

_____

Word Count: _____

Class Summary: _____

_____

_____

_____

_____

Word Count: _____

Words to Go

 BUILD WORD KNOWLEDGE

Complete the meaning and examples for this high-utility word.

Word to Go	Meaning	Examples
achieve a·chieve *verb*	to succeed in accomplishing the _____ you want	My mother always says I can **achieve** anything if I _____ After saving his allowance for six months, Pedro finally **achieved** his goal of _____

 DISCUSS & WRITE EXAMPLES

Discuss your response with a partner. Then complete the sentence in writing.

The musician talked about **achieving** his dreams of stardom after years of

_____

Write your response and read it aloud to a partner.

By the time I turn thirty, I hope to _____ my goal of

_____

 BUILD WORD KNOWLEDGE

Complete the meaning and examples for this high-utility word.

Word to Go	Meaning	Examples
approach ap·proach *noun*	a _____ of dealing with something	The mother's **approach** to caring for her crying baby is to _____ Caitlin tried many **approaches** including _____ to apologize to her friend.

 DISCUSS & WRITE EXAMPLES

Discuss your response with a partner. Then complete the sentence in writing.

The guidance counselor's **approach** to settling arguments is to _____

_____

Write your response and read it aloud to a partner.

I believe in entertaining _____ to exercising, such as

_____

Quote Quest

BUILD FLUENCY

Read Section 3 of the article (*Issues*, pp. 50–51).

ANALYZE TEXT

Record a quote that supports or contradicts your position. Then use a frame to paraphrase the quote.

Quote: _____

_____

_____

_____

Paraphrase: _____

_____

_____

> **Language to PARAPHRASE**
>
> This quote reinforces the idea that _____.
>
> To paraphrase, _____.

SYNTHESIZE IDEAS

Write a topic sentence and two supporting sentences to respond to the quote.

Topic Sentence: I (agree/disagree) with the statement that _____.

_____

_____

_____

Supporting Sentence 1: (For example,/Drawing from my own experience,) _____.

_____

_____

_____

Supporting Sentence 2: (As a result,/Consequently,) _____.

_____

_____

_____

COLLABORATE

Listen attentively as each member of your group reads a quote aloud. Then take turns using a frame to respond.

> **Language to RESPOND**
>
> I noticed this quote also.
>
> This statement caught my attention.
>
> This statement reminded me of _____.
>
> This statement alarmed me as well.

Student Writing Model

Academic Writing Type

A **summary and response** provides an objective overview of the topic and important details from a text and then presents the writer's position on the issue.

A. The **summary** includes a topic sentence, detail sentences, and a concluding sentence.
B. The **response** includes a transitional sentence, a topic sentence that presents the writer's position, supporting details, and a final statement.

ANALYZE TEXT

Read this student model to analyze the elements of a summary and response.

A

In the article titled "The Writing on the Wall," Kim Nguyen explores impacts of graffiti on neighborhoods. Nguyen begins by clarifying opposing arguments about whether graffiti is creative expression or dangerous vandalism. The author continues to address how some communities feel graffiti represents their cultural identity. She explains further that critics of graffiti believe it defaces property. Nguyen concludes by questioning whether graffiti artists can express themselves within the boundaries of law.

B

Whether graffiti should be regarded as art or not is a controversial question. After considering the evidence presented in Nguyen's article and my own experiences, I cannot fully support the idea that graffiti is vandalism. I am in favor of viewing graffiti as art in part because it can be a source of pride for a neighborhood. To illustrate, the article describes how graffiti attracts tourists in San Francisco. My first-hand experiences as a resident of an unattractive city have also helped me understand why graffiti should be created to enhance a neighborhood's beauty. For these reasons, I maintain that graffiti is a relevant form of artistic expression.

MARK & DISCUSS ELEMENTS

Mark the summary and response elements. Then discuss them with your partner.

1. **Underline the writer's position.** *The writer's position is _____.*
2. **Check three reasons or pieces of evidence that support the writer's position.** *One (reason/piece of evidence) is _____.*
3. **Draw boxes around four transition phrases.** *One transition phrase is _____.*
4. **Circle five citation verbs in the essay.** *One citation verb is _____.*
5. **Star five precise topic words.** *An example of a precise topic word is _____.*

Choose Language for Writing

Prompt	Write a summary and response for "Rules of the Road."

IDENTIFY PRECISE WORDS

Review the article to identify and record precise words and phrases for your essay.

Introduction	Section 1	Section 2	Section 3
• priorities	• productive	• deny	• incentive
• driver's license	• policies	• necessity	• _____
• truant	• hardships	• _____	• _____
• _____	• _____	• _____	• _____
• _____	• _____	• _____	• _____

Organize Key Ideas & Details

TAKE NOTES

State the text information to write a topic sentence.

Topic Sentence: In the article titled (title) _____

(author's full name) _____

(citation verb) _____ (topic) _____

_____

List three important details from the article in your own words.

1. _____
_____

2. _____
_____

3. _____
_____

Describe your position and write a topic sentence.

Topic Sentence: After considering the evidence presented in (author's last name + 's)

_____ article and my own experiences, I (can/cannot)

_____ fully support (issue) _____

_____

List reasons and evidence from the text or your experience that supports your position.

Reasons: _____

_____

Evidence: _____

_____

Simple & Complex Sentences

Guidelines for Writing Simple & Complex Sentences

A **simple sentence** contains a subject and a predicate to express a complete thought. A **complex sentence** contains a simple sentence and one or more dependent clauses. A dependent clause cannot stand on its own as a sentence and often begins with a word such as *because*, *since*, or *that*.

Presenting Reasons	Examples
(One/A) significant reason is that ___.	**One significant reason is that** plastic bags take years to decompose.
I am (in favor of/opposed to) ___ in part because ___.	**I am in favor of** banning disposable bags **in part because** they are made from oil.
Due to ___, I am certain that ___.	**Due to** the damage they cause, **I am certain that** plastic bags should be banned.

Presenting Evidence	Examples
To illustrate, ___.	**To illustrate,** plastic bags can take up to 1,000 years to biodegrade.
This is important because ___.	**This is important because** the oil is not a renewable resource.
Based on (current data/recent findings) that show ___, I maintain my position that ___.	**Based on current data that show** plastic bags kill millions of animals yearly, **I maintain my position that** the bags should be banned.

PRESENT REASONS & EVIDENCE

Work with the teacher to write a reason and evidence.

Claim: Graffiti should be viewed as vandalism, not art.

Reason: One reason why I firmly believe that _____

_____ is the fact that _____

Evidence: To illustrate, _____

_____

Work with a partner to write a reason and evidence.

Claim: Schools _____ be responsible for punishing cyberbullies.

Reason: Due to _____

I am certain that _____

Evidence: This is important because _____

_____

Work on your own to write a reason and evidence.

Claim: Girls _____ be allowed to compete on boys' sports teams.

Reason: _____

_____

Evidence: _____

_____

Precise Adjectives to Respond

Guidelines for Using Precise Adjectives to Respond
Precise adjectives help describe nouns more vividly and make your writing more interesting. Use a precise adjective in the transitional sentence of your summary and response essay.

Everyday Adjectives	Precise Adjectives
good	fair, appropriate, worthy, timely
interesting	fascinating, intriguing, thought-provoking, provocative, controversial
hard	difficult, troubling, challenging, complex, complicated, perplexing
silly	absurd, preposterous, ridiculous
untrue	unfounded, groundless, baseless

WRITE PRECISE ADJECTIVES
Complete each transitional sentence with a precise adjective from the chart above.

1. Whether video games harm teens or not is a(n) _____ question.

2. Whether schools should discipline cyberbullies or not is a(n) _____ question.

3. Whether graffiti should be considered a form of artistic expression or not is a(n) _____ question.

Answer each question with a transitional sentence that includes a precise adjective.

Frame: Whether (noun) _____ should (verb phrase) _____ or not is a (precise adjective) _____ question.

1. **Issue:** Should cities outlaw plastic bags?

   Transitional Sentence: _____
   _____

2. **Issue:** Should schools ban unhealthy food?

   Transitional Sentence: _____
   _____

3. **Issue:** Should scientists be able to use animals for research?

   Transitional Sentence: _____
   _____

4. **Issue:** Should girls be allowed to compete on boys' sports teams?

   Transitional Sentence: _____
   _____

Write a Summary & Response

Prompt Write a summary and response for "Rules of the Road."

WRITE AN ESSAY

Use the frame to write a two-paragraph summary and response.

A

In the article titled _____
(title)

_____
(Author's full name)

_____ _____
(citation verb)   (noun phrase: arguments about, impacts of)

_____
(topic)

_____ begins by _____
(Author's last name)   (verb: describing, identifying, clarifying)

_____ .
(important detail)

The author continues to _____
(verb: address, discuss, point out)

_____
(important detail)

_____

(He/She) _____
(citation verb)

further that _____
(important detail)

_____

_____ concludes by _____
(Author's last name)   (verb: emphasizing, suggesting, questioning)

_____
(restate author's conclusion)

B

Whether _____ should _____
(noun)   (verb phrase)

or not is a _____ question. After considering the evidence
(precise adjective)

presented in _____ article and my own experiences, I
(author's last name + 's)

(can/cannot) _____ fully support _____
(issue)

I am _____ _____
(in favor of/opposed to)   (issue)

in part because _____
(reason that supports your position)

To illustrate, _____
(evidence from the article)

_____

My first-hand experiences as a _____
(noun: student, part-time worker, etc.)

have also helped me understand why _____
(reason that supports your position)

_____

For these reasons, I maintain that _____
(your position)

_____

Rate Your Summary & Response

Scoring Guide	
1	Insufficient
2	Developing
3	Sufficient
4	Exemplary

 ASSESS YOUR DRAFT

Rate your summary and response. Then have a partner rate it.

1. Does the summary topic sentence include the title, author, and topic?	Self	1	2	3	4
	Partner	1	2	3	4
2. Did you discuss the most important details in your own words?	Self	1	2	3	4
	Partner	1	2	3	4
3. Did you use present-tense citation verbs to introduce the author's points?	Self	1	2	3	4
	Partner	1	2	3	4
4. Does your response clearly present your position?	Self	1	2	3	4
	Partner	1	2	3	4
5. Does your response include strong reasons and evidence?	Self	1	2	3	4
	Partner	1	2	3	4
6. Did you use correct present- and past-tense verbs in your supporting sentences?	Self	1	2	3	4
	Partner	1	2	3	4
7. Did you use transitions to sequence and introduce supporting points?	Self	1	2	3	4
	Partner	1	2	3	4
8. Did you include precise topic words?	Self	1	2	3	4
	Partner	1	2	3	4
9. Did you use complex sentences to present evidence?	Self	1	2	3	4
	Partner	1	2	3	4
10. Did you conclude with a strong final statement?	Self	1	2	3	4
	Partner	1	2	3	4

REFLECT & REVISE

Record specific priorities and suggestions to help you and your partner revise.

(Partner) Positive Feedback: I appreciate how you (used/included) _____

_____

(Partner) Suggestion: As you revise your summary and response, focus on _____

_____

(Self) Priority 1: My summary and response essay needs _____

_____

(Self) Priority 2: I plan to improve my summary and response by _____

_____

 CHECK & EDIT

Use this checklist to proofread and edit your summary and response.

☐ Did you use commas appropriately in complex sentences?

☐ Did you use present- and past-tense verbs correctly?

☐ Is each sentence complete?

☐ Are all words spelled correctly?

60-Second Speech

IDENTIFY TOPIC
Choose one of the questions below to address in a 60-second speech.

☐ What is the best way to clean up our school environment?

☐ Should our state raise the minimum driving age?

BRAINSTORM IDEAS
Write your claim and two reasons that support it.

My Claim: _____

Reason 1: _____

Reason 2: _____

SYNTHESIZE IDEAS
Take notes on supporting evidence and a counterclaim.

Evidence 1: _____

_____

Evidence 2: _____

_____

Counterclaim: _____

_____

Response: _____

_____

WRITE A SPEECH
Write a 60-second speech that states your claim and includes reasons, evidence, and a counterclaim.

From my point of view, _____

_____

One reason is that _____

_____

Secondly, _____

_____

For example, _____

_____

Critics might claim that _____

However, _____

_____

For these reasons, I _____ that _____

_____

Present & Rate Your Speech

Maintaining a Confident Posture

Posture is how you position your body when addressing an audience. As you deliver your speech, stand up straight and face your audience. Take a deep breath before speaking to help you look confident—instead of rigid—and engage your listeners.

PRESENT YOUR SPEECH

Present your speech to the small group. Make sure to maintain a confident posture.

TAKE NOTES

Listen attentively to your classmates.
Take notes and write if you agree or disagree.

> **Language to AFFIRM & CLARIFY**
>
> I can understand why you see it this way.
> What do you mean by _____?

Classmate's Name	Idea	Agree/ Disagree

ASSESS YOUR SPEECH

Use the Scoring Guide to rate your speech.

1. Did your topic sentence clearly state your claim?	1	2	3	4
2. Did you include strong reasons and evidence to support your claim?	1	2	3	4
3. Did you include precise topic words?	1	2	3	4
4. Did you speak at an appropriate pace?	1	2	3	4
5. Did you use a confident posture?	1	2	3	4

REFLECT

Think of two ways you can improve for your next speech.

Priority 1: In my next speech, I will include _____

_____

_____

Priority 2: When I present my next speech, I will focus on _____

_____

_____

Does the media's focus on beauty have an ugly side?

BUILD KNOWLEDGE

Read and respond to the Data File (*Issues*, p. 52).

BRAINSTORM IDEAS

List types of media and examples of each.

TYPES OF MEDIA	EXAMPLES
• books	• The Hunger Games

PRESENT IDEAS

Use the frames to share ideas with your small group.

• (One/Another) type of media is _____.

• An example of this type of media is _____.

Words to Know

 BUILD WORD KNOWLEDGE
Rate your word knowledge. Then complete the chart for each topic-related word.

| | | ① Don't Know | ② Recognize | ③ Familiar | ④ Know |

Word to Know	Meaning	Example
appearance *noun* ① ② ③ ④	the way that people and objects _____ _____	Most teens are concerned about their **appearance**, but Jolie _____ _____ _____
disorder *noun* ① ② ③ ④	an _____ or _____	Our school provides _____ _____ for students who have learning **disorders**.
diverse *adjective* ① ② ③ ④	very _____ from one another	Sean and Xavier found it difficult to _____ _____ because they had **diverse** opinions.
exposure *noun* ① ② ③ ④	the chance to _____ something	You can avoid too much **exposure** to _____ by _____ _____
ideal *adjective* ① ② ③ ④	the _____ that something or someone can be	_____ is the ideal _____ _____ for me.
media *noun* ① ② ③ ④	organizations that provide _____ _____ to the public	People might pursue jobs in the **media** if they are _____ _____ _____ _____
obsession *noun* ① ② ③ ④	an _____ _____ in something	Some teens have an **obsession** with _____ _____
realistic *adjective* ① ② ③ ④	_____ or _____	Completely replacing plastic bags may not be **realistic**, but _____ _____ _____

Academic Discussion

Do images in the media harm teens' body image?

BRAINSTORM IDEAS

Briefly record at least two ideas.

Agree	Disagree

ANALYZE WORDS

Complete the chart with precise words to discuss and write about the issue.

Everyday	Precise
looks	features,
pretty	attractive,
best	perfect,

MAKE A CLAIM

Rewrite two ideas using the frames and precise words.

1. **Frame:** I would argue that images in the media (do/do not) influence teens based upon _____ (**noun phrase:** conversations, how many teens)

   Response: _____

   _____

2. **Frame:** I have observed that images in the media (harm/do not harm) teens because they are _____ (**adjective:** unrealistic) and _____ (**adjective:** beautiful)

   Response: _____

   _____

COLLABORATE

Listen attentively, restate, and record your partner's idea.

Classmate's Name	Idea

Language to RESTATE
In other words, you have observed that _____.
Yes, that's accurate.
No. What I intended to say was _____.

Ten-Minute Paper

PRESENT IDEAS

Listen attentively, compare ideas, and take notes.
Then write whether you agree or disagree.

Language to COMPARE IDEAS
My observation is similar to _____'s.

Classmate's Name	Idea	Agree/Disagree

ELABORATE IN WRITING

Work with the teacher to write a ten-minute paper.

I have observed that images in the media do not harm teens because they are unrealistic and unconvincing. For example, teens can see that the people shown in the media are too _____ to be _____ models for teens' own appearances. As a result, the _____ of those images on teens is _____

_____

_____

_____

Write a ten-minute paper.

I have observed that images in the media _____ teens because they are _____ and _____

For example, _____

_____

_____

_____

As a result, _____

_____

_____

_____

Words to Go

 BUILD WORD KNOWLEDGE

Complete the meaning and examples for this high-utility word.

Word to Go	Meaning	Examples
image im·age *noun*	a _____ or a _____, which might be real or imagined	An **image** that you might see in an advertisement is _____ _____ I have an **image** of my ideal _____ in my mind.

DISCUSS & WRITE EXAMPLES

Discuss your response with a partner. Then complete the sentence in writing.

Online, people should only share **images** that _____

_____

Write your response and read it aloud to a partner.

News _____ of _____

_____ can be difficult to view.

 BUILD WORD KNOWLEDGE

Complete the meaning and examples for this high-utility word.

Word to Go	Meaning	Examples
percent per·cent *noun*	a _____ of a whole, measured by _____ in one hundred	In the school election, more than 70 **percent** of the students voted for _____ _____ The basketball team hopes to win _____ **percent** of its games.

DISCUSS & WRITE EXAMPLES

Discuss your response with a partner. Then complete the sentence in writing.

About 10 **percent** of the students in my school _____

_____

Write your response and read it aloud to a partner.

Because there was a 75 _____ chance of rain, the parade

organizers _____

Language to Summarize

BUILD FLUENCY
Read the article introduction and Section 1 (*Issues*, pp. 53–54).

ASK & ANSWER QUESTIONS
Take turns asking and answering questions with a partner.

Q: What is the author's **main point**?

A: The author's **main point** is _____.

Q: What are the most **relevant details** in this section?

A: One **relevant detail** in this section is _____.

A: Another **relevant detail** in this section is _____.

Section Shrink

SUMMARIZE
Complete the topic and important details for Section 1. Then "shrink" the section by writing a summary in 35 or fewer words.

Topic (Who?/What?):   images in the media

Important Details: • The media show skinny women and muscular men because

_____

• A fashion insider asserts that _____

_____

• Photos are often touched up to _____

_____

• Opponents of misleading media images argue that _____

_____

Partner Summary: The media images of _____

_____ are _____

_____ but

_____

Word Count: _____

Class Summary: _____

_____

_____

_____

Word Count: _____

Words to Go

 BUILD WORD KNOWLEDGE

Complete the meaning and examples for this high-utility word.

Word to Go	Meaning	Examples
perceive per·ceive *verb*	to _____ or _____ of someone or something in a certain way	My older sister **perceives** herself as _____ but in reality _____ _____ Quiet people are sometimes **perceived** as _____

DISCUSS EXAMPLES

Discuss your response with a partner. Then complete the sentence in writing.

I care about how I am **perceived** by _____

so I _____

BUILD WORD KNOWLEDGE

Complete the meaning and examples for this high-utility word.

Word to Go	Meaning	Examples
perception per·cep·tion *noun*	the way something is _____ _____ and the _____ of what it is like	My neighborhood _____ _____ so there is a **perception** that _____ _____ When I was younger, my **perception** of _____ was that _____ _____

DISCUSS EXAMPLES

Discuss your response with a partner. Then complete the sentence in writing.

I'm known for _____ but I hope to change people's

perception of me by _____

WRITE EXAMPLES

Write your response and read it aloud to a partner.

Most of my friends _____ me as (a/an) _____

_____ person.

Before I became addicted to video games, my _____ of them

was that _____

Language to Summarize

📖 BUILD FLUENCY

Read Section 2 of the article (*Issues*, pp. 54–55).

💬 ASK & ANSWER QUESTIONS

Take turns asking and answering questions with a partner.

Q: What is this section **primarily about**?

A: This section is **primarily about** _____.

Q: What are the most **vital details** in this section?

A: One **vital detail** in this section is _____.

A: Another **vital detail** in this section is _____.

Section Shrink

 SUMMARIZE

Complete the topic and important details for Section 2. Then "shrink" the section by writing a summary in 35 or fewer words.

Topic (Who?/What?):   media's negative impact on _____

Important Details: • The eating disorder anorexia nervosa _____

_____

• Critics of the media point out that _____

_____

• A researcher on body image thinks the unrealistic images

_____

• _____

_____

Partner Summary: Media critics believe that _____

contribute(s) to _____

_____ but _____

_____

Word Count: _____

Class Summary: _____

_____

_____

_____

Word Count: _____

Words to Go

 BUILD WORD KNOWLEDGE

Complete the meaning and examples for this high-utility word.

Word to Go	Meaning	Examples
appropriate ap·pro·pri·ate *adjective*	_____ or _____ for a situation	I wanted to _____ but my mother said that was not appropriate for _____ _____ Would _____ be an appropriate gift for _____ _____

DISCUSS & WRITE EXAMPLES

Discuss your response with a partner. Then complete the sentence in writing.

The reason I am not allowed to _____

is because _____ thinks it is not **appropriate**.

Write your response and read it aloud to a partner.

I wanted to tell my best friend what had happened, but I thought a more

_____ time to talk would be _____

BUILD WORD KNOWLEDGE

Complete the meaning and examples for this high-utility word.

Word to Go	Meaning	Examples
reaction re·ac·tion *noun*	something that a person _____ or _____ in response to something	When I _____ _____ my family's reaction was _____ _____ Marla's reaction to _____ _____ was to _____ _____

DISCUSS & WRITE EXAMPLES

Discuss your response with a partner. Then complete the sentence in writing.

I knew _____ when I saw my teacher's

reaction to _____

Write your response and read it aloud to a partner.

Most teens probably feel that getting grounded is an extreme _____

to _____

Quote Quest

BUILD FLUENCY
Read Section 3 of the article (*Issues*, pp. 56–57).

ANALYZE TEXT
Record a quote that supports or contradicts your
position. Then use a frame to paraphrase the quote.

Quote: _____

_____

_____

_____

Paraphrase: _____

_____

_____

> **Language to PARAPHRASE**
>
> To paraphrase, _____.
>
> The author seems to be
> saying that _____.

SYNTHESIZE IDEAS
Write a topic sentence and two supporting sentences to respond to the quote.

Topic Sentence: I (agree/disagree) with the statement that _____.

_____

_____

_____

Supporting Sentence 1: (For example,/Drawing from my own experience,) _____.

_____

_____

_____

Supporting Sentence 2: (As a result,/Consequently,) _____.

_____

_____

_____

COLLABORATE
Listen attentively as each member of your
group reads a quote aloud. Then take turns
using a frame to respond.

> **Language to RESPOND**
>
> This quote (supports/contradicts)
> my opinion.
>
> This statement intrigued me.
>
> I found this statement alarming.
>
> This statement reminded me of my
> experiences.

Student Writing Model

Academic Writing Type

An **argument** states a claim and supports it with reasons and evidence from sources.

    A. The **introduction** clearly states the writer's claim about the issue.

    B. **Detail paragraphs** support the claim with reasons and evidence. The writer may also present counterclaims and respond with strong evidence.

    C. The **conclusion** strongly restates the writer's claim about the issue.

🔍 ANALYZE TEXT

Read this student model to analyze the elements of an argument.

A

After examining the issues surrounding the media and self-image, I agree wholeheartedly that the media are not responsible for teens' body images.

B

One reason I maintain this position is that the media often show healthy images. In the article "The Ugly Effects of Beauty," Marcos Cano presents compelling data regarding the positive effect of media images. For example, the editor of *Men's Health* explains that his magazine shows what fit men look like (Cano 57). Critics of these images tend to point out that they make boys take extreme measures (Cano 56). However, to subscribe to the notion that media images damage boys' health is unfounded. Studies actually demonstrate that only 2 percent of boys use steroids (Cano 56).

I am also opposed to regulating media images due to teens' knowledge that the pictures are not real. Pedro Gutierrez emphasizes in "The Image Artist" that retouching creates ideal images to sell products (60). One particularly convincing statistic is that female models typically "weigh 23 percent less than the average woman" (Cano 55).

C

Whether media images harm teens will no doubt remain a controversial issue. After reviewing relevant data and reflecting on my own experiences, I still contend that the media cannot be held accountable for teens' self-images.

💬 MARK & DISCUSS ELEMENTS

Mark the argument elements and use the frames to discuss them with your partner.

1. **Underline the writer's claim.** *The writer's claim is that _____.*

2. **Check two reasons and four pieces of evidence that support the writer's claim.**
   One (reason/piece of evidence) that supports the writer's claim is _____.

3. **Draw a box around a counterclaim.** *One counterclaim is _____.*

4. **Circle three verb phrases that express opinions.** *One verb phrase is _____.*

5. **Star six precise adjectives.** *An example of a precise adjective is _____.*

Choose Language for Writing

Prompt	Do the media harm teens' self-images? Write an argument that states your claim and supports it with text evidence.

 GATHER TEXT EVIDENCE
Read Articles 2 and 3 in the *Issues* book (pp. 58–61).

 IDENTIFY PRECISE WORDS
Review the articles to identify precise words and phrases for your argument.

Article 1		Article 2	Article 3
• anorexia nervosa	• retouch artist	• reaction	• perfect
• attribute	• consequences	• _____	• _____
• _____	• _____	• _____	• _____
• _____	• _____	• _____	• _____
• _____	• _____	• _____	• _____

Organize Evidence & Counterclaims

 TAKE NOTES
Use academic language to state your claim and write an introduction.

Introduction: After examining the issues surrounding (topic) _____

_____

I (agree/disagree) _____ that (your claim) _____

List two reasons that support your claim and text evidence for each reason.

Reason 1: _____

Evidence: _____

Reason 2: _____

Evidence: _____

List a counterclaim and respond with strong evidence.

Counterclaim: _____

Response: _____

Citing Sources

Guidelines for Citing Sources

Citations give credit for other people's ideas. They also help readers find the original information if they want to learn more.

To **cite a source**, use quotation marks around direct quotes or paraphrase the author's ideas in your own words. Identify the source in parentheses and put the period after the citation.

Type of Citation	Directions	Examples
when a source has one author	include the author's last name followed by the page number	Many teens develop negative self-images because of the thousands of "skinny women and muscular men" they see in the media every day (Cano 53). For example, Jason Dean became obsessed with working out to obtain muscles like the ones he saw in magazines (Cano 56).
when the author's name is in the sentence	include the page number only	According to Pedro Gutierrez, Kate Winslet was upset when images were altered to make her look thinner (60).
when a source has two authors	include the authors' last names in the same order as the source	Critics of a lower minimum wage for teens argue that employers might lay off adults and hire teens to save money (Alvarez and Martinez 61–62).

✎ WRITE CITATIONS

Rewrite each sentence with a citation and proper punctuation.

1. After Holly Hurt became obsessed with losing weight, she needed months of treatment to overcome anorexia.

   _____

   _____

   _____

2. According to Marcos Cano, eating disorders affect about five million people.

   _____

   _____

   _____

3. The photo retoucher Pascal Dangin claims that people should "realize that most fashion and advertising photos are retouched."

   _____

   _____

   _____

Verb Phrases to Express Opinions

Opinion	Verb Phrases to Express an Opinion	Argument Examples
agree	*agree wholeheartedly that* *still maintain that* *still contend that* *am convinced that*	After examining the issues, I **agree wholeheartedly that** the media should choose images that reflect people's diversity. One reason I **am convinced that** teens are aware of image retouching is that my friends often discuss the topic.
disagree	*disagree entirely that* *cannot support the opinion that* *still contend that* *am not convinced that*	After reflecting on my experiences, I **disagree entirely that** we need laws to restrict what images can appear in magazines. One reason I **cannot support the opinion that** media images do not affect teens is that they see thousands of them every day.
undecided	*am undecided about whether* *see both sides of the issue* *am more inclined to believe*	Although the article presents interesting information, I **am undecided about whether** most models promote unhealthy bodies. Due to the evidence presented, I **see both sides of the issue**.

IDENTIFY VERB PHRASES

Circle the verb phrases in the chart that you plan to use in your argument. Then complete each sentence with a verb phrase to express an opinion.

1. After reading the article, I _____
   teens need to be educated about healthy body images.

2. Despite the evidence presented, I _____
   retouching photographs is harmless.

3. For these reasons, I _____
   media images influence teens to become anorexic.

WRITE OPINIONS

Write sentences that express the opinion in parentheses. Include details from texts.

1. **(agree)** After examining the issues surrounding media images, I _____

   _____

2. **(disagree)** After reviewing recent data and reflecting on my own experiences, I _____

   _____

3. **(undecided)** Based on the facts in the articles, I _____

   _____

Write an Argument

Prompt | Do the media harm teens' self-images? Write an argument that states your claim and supports it with text evidence.

 WRITE A RESEARCH PAPER
Use the frame to write your introduction, detail paragraphs, and conclusion.

A

After examining the issues surrounding _____
(topic)

I _____ that _____
(verb/verb phrase to express opinion)   (strongly state your claim)

_____

B

One reason I maintain this position is that _____
(first reason that supports your claim)

_____

The article _____ presents _____
(title of article)   (adjective)

data regarding the (positive/negative) _____ consequences of

media images on teens. For example, _____
(evidence from article)

_____

(Opponents/Proponents) _____ of _____
(topic)

_____ tend to _____
(verb)

_____
(counterclaim)

However, (current data/studies) _____ actually demonstrate

_____
(your response to the counterclaim)

_____

I am also (in favor of/opposed to) _____ _____
(topic)

_____ due to _____
(second reason that supports your claim)

_____
(Author's full name)   emphasizes in _____
(title of article)

that _____
(evidence from a different article)

One particularly _____ statistic is _____
(adjective)   (statistic from a source)

_____

C

Whether _____
(restate the issue)

will remain a controversial issue. After reviewing _____ data,
(adjective)

I _____ that _____
(verb/verb phrase to express opinion)   (restate your claim)

_____

Rate Your Argument

 ASSESS YOUR DRAFT

Rate your argument research paper. Then have a partner rate it.

Scoring Guide	
1	Insufficient
2	Developing
3	Sufficient
4	Exemplary

1. Does the introduction clearly state your claim?	Self	1	2	3	4
	Partner	1	2	3	4
2. Did you include strong reasons and evidence to support your claim?	Self	1	2	3	4
	Partner	1	2	3	4
3. Did you include a counterclaim and respond with strong evidence?	Self	1	2	3	4
	Partner	1	2	3	4
4. Did you include precise topic words?	Self	1	2	3	4
	Partner	1	2	3	4
5. Did you include citation information for evidence from texts?	Self	1	2	3	4
	Partner	1	2	3	4
6. Did you use strong verbs and verb phrases to express opinions?	Self	1	2	3	4
	Partner	1	2	3	4
7. Did you include a variety of sentences (simple, compound, complex)?	Self	1	2	3	4
	Partner	1	2	3	4

 REFLECT & REVISE

Record specific priorities and suggestions to help you and your partner revise.

(Partner) Positive Feedback: I appreciate your (effort to/use of/skillful) _____

_____

_____

(Partner) Suggestion: As you revise your argument, make a point of _____

_____

_____

(Self) Priority 1: I plan to focus the revision of my argument on _____

_____

_____

(Self) Priority 2: One revision I plan to implement is to _____

_____

_____

✓ **CHECK & EDIT**

Use this checklist to proofread and edit your argument.

☐ Did you format citations correctly?

☐ Did you use commas appropriately after transitions?

☐ Did you use verb tenses appropriately?

☐ Are all words spelled correctly?

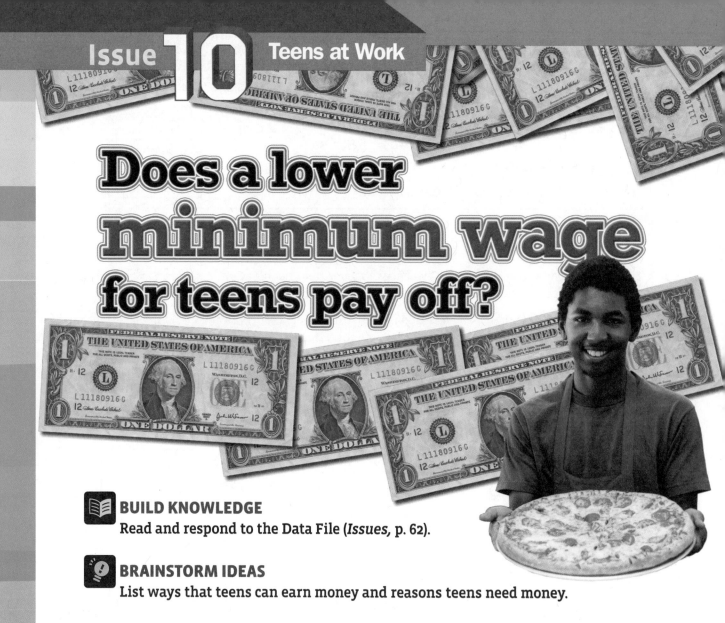

Does a lower minimum wage for teens pay off?

BUILD KNOWLEDGE
Read and respond to the Data File (*Issues*, p. 62).

BRAINSTORM IDEAS
List ways that teens can earn money and reasons teens need money.

WAYS FOR TEENS TO EARN MONEY	REASONS TEENS NEED MONEY

PRESENT IDEAS
Use the frames to share ideas with your small group.

• (One/Another) way that teens can earn money is _____.

• Teens require money (for/to) _____.

Words to Know

BUILD WORD KNOWLEDGE

Rate your word knowledge. Then complete the chart for each topic-related word.

	① Don't Know	② Recognize	③ Familiar	④ Know

Word to Know	Meaning	Example
compensation *noun* ① ② ③ ④	the _____ a person receives for _____	My neighbor gave me $10 as compensation for _____
earnings *noun* ① ② ③ ④	the _____ _____ for the work he or she does	Ciara keeps her **earnings** from _____ _____ in the bank.
economy *noun* ① ② ③ ④	the system by which _____ _____ are produced and used within a country or area	Because of the struggling **economy**, many teens are _____ _____ _____ _____
employment *noun* ① ② ③ ④	the condition of _____ _____	Isaac will be able to _____ _____ _____ once he finds part-time **employment**.
income *noun* ① ② ③ ④	_____ that a person regularly _____ _____	Earning a steady **income** may be challenging if you _____ _____
increase *verb* ① ② ③ ④	to make or become _____ _____	We were happy that the principal decided to **increase** _____ _____ _____
rate *noun* ① ② ③ ④	the number of times that _____ _____ during a period of time	Because of the high rainfall **rate** last fall, _____ _____
reduced *adjective* ① ② ③ ④	_____ _____ than it was before	The cafeteria's healthier menu resulted in a **reduced** number of _____ _____

Academic Discussion

Should the minimum wage be the same for teens and adults?

BRAINSTORM IDEAS

Briefly record at least two ideas.

Agree	Disagree

ANALYZE WORDS

Complete the chart with precise words to discuss and write about the issue.

Everyday	Precise
work (noun)	position,
lower (verb)	decrease,
pay (noun)	wage,

MAKE A CLAIM

Rewrite two ideas using the frames and precise words.

1. **Frame:** I would argue that the minimum wage (should/should not) be the same for teens and adults because of _____ (**noun phrase**).

   Response: _____

   _____

2. **Frame:** From my point of view, the minimum wage (should/should not) be the same for teens and adults when _____ (**independent clause**).

   Response: _____

   _____

   _____

COLLABORATE

Listen attentively, restate, and record your partner's idea.

Classmate's Name	Idea

Language to RESTATE

In other words, your point of view is that _____.

Yes, that's accurate.

No. What I intended to say was _____.

Ten-Minute Paper

PRESENT IDEAS

Listen attentively, compare ideas, and take notes.
Then write whether you agree or disagree.

Language to COMPARE IDEAS
My point of view is related to _____'s.

Classmate's Name	Idea	Agree/Disagree

ELABORATE IN WRITING

Work with the teacher to write a ten-minute paper.

From my point of view, the minimum wage should not be the same for teens and adults when a reduced wage might make more jobs available for teens. For example, decreasing teens' compensation would help businesses _____
_____ .

As a result, those businesses would _____
_____

and be able to _____
to more teens.

Write a ten-minute paper.

From my point of view, the minimum wage _____ be the same
for teens and adults when _____
_____
_____

For example, _____
_____
_____

As a result, _____
_____
_____
_____

Words to Go

 BUILD WORD KNOWLEDGE
Complete the meaning and examples for this high-utility word.

Word to Go	Meaning	Examples
circumstances cir·cum·stan·ces *noun*	_____ or _____ that are connected to a situation or event	I would only _____ _____ under special **circumstances**. One of the **circumstances** that led to my friend canceling our plans was that _____ _____ _____

💬 **DISCUSS & WRITE EXAMPLES**
Discuss your response with a partner. Then complete the sentence in writing.

Under no **circumstances** should drivers _____

unless _____

Write your response and read it aloud to a partner.

_____ that might keep someone from getting to school on time

include _____

📘 **BUILD WORD KNOWLEDGE**
Complete the meaning and examples for this high-utility word.

Word to Go	Meaning	Examples
minimum min·i·mum *adjective*	describing the _____ number or amount allowed or needed	The **minimum** amount of time it will take me to make dinner is _____ _____ Our country has laws that set the **minimum** _____ _____

💬 **DISCUSS & WRITE EXAMPLES**
Discuss your response with a partner. Then complete the sentence in writing.

If you want to become a _____ you should spend a **minimum** time of

three hours a week _____

Write your response and read it aloud to a partner.

The _____ amount of sleep I need to be alert the next morning is

_____

Language to Summarize

BUILD FLUENCY
Read the article introduction and Section 1 (*Issues*, pp. 63–64).

ASK & ANSWER QUESTIONS
Take turns asking and answering questions with a partner.

Q: What is the author's **main point**?

A: The author's **main point** is _____.

Q: What are the most **relevant details** in this section?

A: One **relevant detail** in this section is _____.

A: Another **relevant detail** in this section is _____.

Section Shrink

SUMMARIZE
Complete the topic and important details for Section 1. Then "shrink" the section by writing a summary in 35 or fewer words.

Topic (Who?/What?):   reasons to reduce the minimum wage for teens

Important Details: • According to an economist, teens _____

   • A labor analyst argues that lowering the minimum wage for

   teens _____

   • Research shows that increases in the minimum wage have

   contributed to _____

   • Economists and experts also agree that a reduced minimum

   wage would _____ and help teens

   _____

Partner Summary: Many economists agree that _____

   _____ which would _____

   _____ and _____

   _____

Word Count: _____

Class Summary: _____

   _____

   _____

   _____

Word Count: _____

Words to Go

 BUILD WORD KNOWLEDGE

Complete the meaning and examples for this high-utility word.

Word to Go	Meaning	Examples
shift shift *verb*	to _____ attention, direction, or focus from one thing to another	If the wind doesn't **shift** direction, the fire might _____ _____ The teacher's attention **shifted** from the board when _____ _____ _____

 DISCUSS & WRITE EXAMPLES

Discuss your response with a partner. Then complete the sentence in writing.

Fashion trends tend to **shift** often, which can lead teens to _____

_____

Write your response and read it aloud to a partner.

I _____ my support to a different sports team after _____

_____

BUILD WORD KNOWLEDGE

Complete the meaning and examples for this high-utility word.

Word to Go	Meaning	Examples
sufficient suf·fi·cient *adjective*	_____ for a specific purpose	Before believing that a friend _____ I would need **sufficient** evidence. Teens who consume more than a **sufficient** number of calories can _____ _____

DISCUSS & WRITE EXAMPLES

Discuss your response with a partner. Then complete the sentence in writing.

_____ is **sufficient** compensation for _____

_____

Write your response and read it aloud to a partner.

One week is not a _____ amount of time to prepare if you want to

_____

Language to Summarize

BUILD FLUENCY

Read Section 2 of the article (*Issues*, pp. 64–66).

ASK & ANSWER QUESTIONS

Take turns asking and answering questions with a partner.

Q: What is this section **primarily about**?

A: This section is **primarily about** _____.

Q: What are the most **vital details** in this section?

A: One **vital detail** in this section is _____.

A: Another **vital detail** in this section is _____.

Section Shrink

SUMMARIZE

Complete the topic and important details for Section 2. Then "shrink" the section by writing a summary in 35 or fewer words.

Topic (Who?/What?):   reasons to _____

Important Details: • Opponents of a reduced minimum wage for teens _____

_____

• During a difficult economy, _____

_____

• Labor unions are concerned that _____

_____

_____

• _____

_____

Partner Summary: Opponents of a reduced minimum wage for teens _____

_____

_____ and _____

_____

Word Count: _____

Class Summary: _____

_____

_____

_____

Word Count: _____

Words to Go

 BUILD WORD KNOWLEDGE
Complete the meaning and examples for this high-utility word.

Word to Go	Meaning	Examples
aspect as·pect *noun*	one of the _____ of a situation, plan, or idea	One **aspect** of camping I might find difficult is _____ _____ A healthier body can be one of the positive **aspects** of _____ _____

DISCUSS & WRITE EXAMPLES
Discuss your response with a partner. Then complete the sentence in writing.

I sometimes have to help my parents _____

_____ because they don't understand some **aspects** of technology.

Write your response and read it aloud to a partner.

Perhaps the most harmful _____ of the media's obsession with

beauty is _____

BUILD WORD KNOWLEDGE
Complete the meaning and examples for this high-utility word.

Word to Go	Meaning	Examples
option op·tion *noun*	a _____	Riding my bike to the store doesn't seem like the best **option** because _____ _____ Once a play starts, a quarterback has only a few seconds to consider his **options** before _____ _____

DISCUSS & WRITE EXAMPLES
Discuss your response with a partner. Then complete the sentence in writing.

As a teen, I don't have the **option** to _____

because _____

Write your response and read it aloud to a partner.

Some victims of cyberbullying feel that the only _____ they have

to avoid harassment is _____

Quote Quest

BUILD FLUENCY
Read Section 3 of the article (*Issues*, pp. 66–67).

ANALYZE TEXT
Record a quote that supports or contradicts your position. Then use a frame to paraphrase the quote.

Quote: _____
_____
_____
_____

Language to PARAPHRASE
The author seems to be saying that _____.
In this quote, the author provides a compelling (example of/reason for) _____.

Paraphrase: _____
_____
_____

SYNTHESIZE IDEAS
Write a topic sentence and two supporting sentences to respond to the quote.

Topic Sentence: I (agree/disagree) with the statement that _____.
_____
_____
_____

Supporting Sentence 1: (For example,/Drawing from my own experience,) _____.
_____
_____
_____

Supporting Sentence 2: (As a result,/Consequently,) _____.
_____
_____
_____

COLLABORATE
Listen attentively as each member of your group reads a quote aloud. Then take turns using a frame to respond.

Language to RESPOND
This quote (supports/contradicts) my opinion.
This statement intrigued me.
I found this statement alarming.
This statement reminded me of my experiences.

Student Writing Model

Academic Writing Type

An **argument** states a claim and supports it with reasons and evidence from sources.

A. The **introduction** clearly states the writer's claim about the issue.
B. **Detail paragraphs** support the claim with reasons and evidence. The writer may also present counterclaims and respond with strong evidence.
C. The **conclusion** strongly restates the writer's claim about the issue.

ANALYZE TEXT

Read this student model to analyze the elements of an argument.

A

After examining the issues surrounding minimum wages, I am convinced that the minimum wage should not be lower for teens than for adults.

B

One reason I maintain this position is that adults need jobs more than teens. In the article "Help (Not) Wanted," Chris Alvarez and Julia Martinez present strong data regarding the negative consequences of a lower minimum wage for teens. To illustrate, in a recession, jobs might go to teens if employers could pay them less, leaving adults who need to support their families unemployed (Alvarez and Martinez 65). Proponents of a reduced minimum wage for teens tend to highlight that it would give teens work experience. Current data actually demonstrate that teens are "striving for higher levels of education," which should help them find better jobs in the future (Alvarez and Martinez 67).

I am also opposed to a lower minimum wage due to the experiences of Robert Partyka. Marissa Menendez emphasizes in "Scraping for College" that a lower minimum wage would mean Partyka would have to take fewer courses, delaying his degree (68). One particularly intriguing statistic is that 45 percent of teens would be unwilling to accept a lower training wage of $5.25 (Khan 71).

C

Whether the minimum wage should be the same for adults and teens will remain a controversial issue. After reviewing recent data, I still cannot support the opinion that the minimum wage should be less for teens than for adults.

MARK & DISCUSS ELEMENTS

Mark the argument elements and use the frames to discuss them with your partner.

1. **Underline the writer's claim.** *The writer's claim is that _____.*

2. **Check two reasons and four pieces of evidence that support the writer's claim.** *One (reason/piece of evidence) that supports the writer's claim is _____.*

3. **Draw a box around a counterclaim.** *One counterclaim is _____.*

4. **Circle three verb phrases that express opinions.** *One verb phrase is _____.*

5. **Star five precise adjectives.** *An example of a precise adjective is _____.*

Choose Language for Writing

Prompt	Should the minimum wage be the same for teens and adults? Write an argument that states your claim and supports it with text evidence.

 GATHER TEXT EVIDENCE

Read Articles 2 and 3 in the *Issues* book (pp. 68–71).

 IDENTIFY PRECISE WORDS

Review the articles to identify precise words and phrases for your argument.

Article 1		Article 2	Article 3
• job seekers	• _____	• part-time job	• training wage
• labor market	• _____	• tuition	• _____
• job applications	• _____	• _____	• _____
• _____	• _____	• _____	• _____
• _____	• _____	• _____	• _____

Organize Evidence & Counterclaims

 TAKE NOTES

Use academic language to state your claim and write an introduction.

Introduction: After examining the issues surrounding (topic) _____

_____

I (agree/disagree) _____ that (your claim) _____

_____

List two reasons that support your claim and text evidence for each reason.

Reason 1: _____

_____

Evidence: _____

_____

Reason 2: _____

_____

Evidence: _____

_____

List a counterclaim and respond with strong evidence.

Counterclaim: _____

_____

Response: _____

_____

Conditional Verbs

Guidelines for Using Conditional Verbs

Conditional verbs describe what might or could happen. They show what conditions would be like if a recommendation became reality.

A real future possibility: will, shall, can, may (+ base verb)

Keeping the minimum wage equal will ensure that teens earn as much as adults.

An uncertain future possibility: would, should, could, might (+ base verb)

If teens earn less than adults, it might result in more jobs for teens.

A past impossibility: would have, should have, could have, might have (+ past participle)

During the last recession, teens would have benefited from a lower minimum wage.

 IDENTIFY CONDITIONAL VERBS

Read the argument and circle the conditional verbs.

> After examining the issues surrounding the idea of restricting the number of hours teens can work each week, I agree that setting a limit would benefit teens. One reason I maintain this position is that teens who work too many hours often neglect other responsibilities. In the online article "Teen 'Training Wage' Bill Draws Opposition," Matt Wickenheiser presents strong data regarding the negative consequences that can result from teens working an unlimited number of hours. For example, teens who work many hours during school periods may sacrifice homework or sleep, putting their grades at risk (Wickenheiser). Opponents of limiting teens' working hours tend to point out that in difficult economic times, many teens need to work as many hours as possible. However, school should be teens' first priority. After reviewing the substantial data, I conclude that teens should limit their working hours so that they may focus on education.

 WRITE CONDITIONAL VERBS

Use a conditional verb to complete each sentence.

1. If teen workers had found more jobs last year, _____

   _____

2. If employers pay adult workers more than teens, _____

   _____

3. As long as the minimum wage stays the same for teens and adults, _____

   _____

4. If the unemployment rate drops, _____

   _____

5. Assuming that business owners receive a tax credit for hiring teens, _____

   _____

Transitions to Introduce Evidence

Type of Evidence	Transitions	Examples
From Text or Experience	*For example,* *For instance,* *To illustrate,* *As an illustration,*	**For instance,** the minimum wage increased by 41 percent in just two years. **As an illustration,** the online article states that the unemployment rate for teens is significantly higher than it is for adults.
From Experience	*Based on my experiences,* *Drawing from my family life,* *In my personal life,* *Within my (group of friends/school/city),* *As a(n) (athlete/student/teen),*	**Drawing from my family life,** when my older sister got a job that paid a training wage, she wanted to do well to prove that she was worth more. **In my personal life,** I've had a job that paid the minimum wage, and one that paid a training wage. **As a teen,** I feel that getting paid less for the same work as an adult is insulting.

IDENTIFY TRANSITIONS

Circle the transitions in the chart that you plan to use in your argument.
Then complete each sentence with an appropriate transition.

1. _____ in 2010 the unemployment rate for teens was 28 percent, according to the United States Bureau of Labor Statistics.

2. _____ none of the teens I know have after-school jobs.

3. _____ employers can pay workers under the age of 20 only $4.25 an hour.

4. _____ I believe the experience a part-time job provides is as valuable as the income.

WRITE SUPPORTING DETAILS

Write three supporting details using transitions to introduce evidence.

1. _____   _____
   (Transition)   (evidence from text)

   _____

   _____

2. _____   _____
   (Transition)   (evidence from experience)

   _____

   _____

3. _____.   _____
   (Transition)   (evidence from text or experience)

   _____

   _____

Write an Argument

Prompt | Should the minimum wage be the same for teens and adults? Write an argument that states your claim and supports it with text evidence.

 WRITE A RESEARCH PAPER
Use the frame to write your introduction, detail paragraphs, and conclusion.

A

After examining the issues surrounding _____
(topic)

I _____ that _____
(verb/verb phrase to express opinion)   (strongly state your claim)

_____

B

One reason I maintain this position is that _____
(first reason that supports your claim)

_____

The article _____ presents _____
(title of article)   (adjective)

data regarding the (positive/negative) _____ consequences

of a lower minimum wage for teens. _____
(Transition introducing evidence)

_____
(evidence from article)

_____

(Opponents/Proponents) _____ of _____
(topic)

_____ tend to _____
(verb)

_____
(counterclaim)

_____ (Current data/Studies) _____

actually demonstrate that _____
(your response to the counterclaim)

_____

I am also (in favor of/opposed to) _____

_____ due to _____
(topic)   (second reason that supports your claim)

_____

_____ emphasizes in _____ that
(Author's full name)   (title of article)

_____
(evidence from a different article)

One particularly _____ statistic is _____
(adjective)   (statistic from a source)

_____

C

Whether _____
(restate the issue)

will remain a controversial issue. After reviewing _____ data,
(adjective)

I _____ that _____
(verb/verb phrase to express opinion)   (restate your claim)

_____

Rate Your Argument

 ASSESS YOUR DRAFT

Rate your argument research paper. Then have a partner rate it.

1. Does the introduction clearly state your claim?	Self	1	2	3	4
	Partner	1	2	3	4
2. Did you include strong reasons and evidence to support your claim?	Self	1	2	3	4
	Partner	1	2	3	4
3. Did you include a counterclaim and respond with strong evidence?	Self	1	2	3	4
	Partner	1	2	3	4
4. Did you include precise topic words?	Self	1	2	3	4
	Partner	1	2	3	4
5. Did you include citation information for evidence from texts?	Self	1	2	3	4
	Partner	1	2	3	4
6. Did you use strong verbs and verb phrases to express opinions?	Self	1	2	3	4
	Partner	1	2	3	4
7. Did you include transitions to introduce reasons and evidence?	Self	1	2	3	4
	Partner	1	2	3	4
8. Did you include a variety of sentences (simple, compound, complex)?	Self	1	2	3	4
	Partner	1	2	3	4

 REFLECT & REVISE

Record specific priorities and suggestions to help you and your partner revise.

(Partner) Positive Feedback: I appreciated your (efforts to/use of/skillful) _____

_____

(Partner) Suggestion: As you revise your argument, make a point of _____

_____

(Self) Priority 1: I plan to focus the revision of my argument on _____

_____

(Self) Priority 2: One revision I plan to implement is to _____

_____

✓ **CHECK & EDIT**

Use this checklist to proofread and edit your argument.

- ☐ Did you format citations correctly?
- ☐ Did you use commas appropriately after transitions?
- ☐ Did you use verb tenses appropriately?
- ☐ Are all words spelled correctly?

60-Second Speech

IDENTIFY TOPIC

Choose one of the questions below to address in a 60-second speech.

☐ Should our school do more to promote healthy self-images?

☐ Should our community do more to help teens find jobs?

BRAINSTORM IDEAS

Write your claim and two reasons that support it.

My Claim: _____

Reason 1: _____

Reason 2: _____

SYNTHESIZE IDEAS

Take notes on supporting evidence and a counterclaim.

Evidence 1: _____

_____

Evidence 2: _____

_____

Counterclaim: _____

_____

Response: _____

_____

WRITE A SPEECH

Write a 60-second speech that states your claim and includes reasons, evidence, and a counterclaim.

From my perspective, _____

_____

First, _____

_____

In addition, _____

_____

For example, _____

_____

Although some people contend that _____

_____

I maintain that _____

In conclusion, I believe that _____

_____

Present & Rate Your Speech

Ensuring Clear Pronunciation

Pronunciation is how you say words. When you give a speech, make sure that you don't mumble and that you pronounce sounds properly. For example, make sure you say "going to" instead of "gonna."

PRESENT YOUR SPEECH
Present your speech to the small group. Make sure to maintain eye contact.

TAKE NOTES
Listen attentively to your classmates.
Take notes and write if you agree or disagree.

Language to AFFIRM & CLARIFY
That's an intriguing perspective.
What exactly do you mean by _____?

Classmate's Name	Idea	Agree/Disagree

ASSESS YOUR SPEECH
Use the Scoring Guide to rate your speech.

Scoring Guide			
1	Insufficient	3	Sufficient
2	Developing	4	Exemplary

	1	2	3	4
1. Did your topic sentence clearly state your claim?	1	2	3	4
2. Did you include strong reasons and evidence to support your speech?	1	2	3	4
3. Did you include precise topic words?	1	2	3	4
4. Did you maintain appropriate posture?	1	2	3	4
5. Did you use clear pronunciation?	1	2	3	4

REFLECT
Think of two ways you can improve for your next speech.

Priority 1: I can improve my next speech by _____

_____

Priority 2: When I present my next speech, I will focus on _____

_____

_____

Does drug testing keep schools safe— or put your rights at risk?

 BUILD KNOWLEDGE
Read and respond to the Data File (*Issues*, p. 72).

 BRAINSTORM IDEAS
List ways that drugs can impact a teen's health, school work, and family life.

IMPACT OF DRUGS

HEALTH	SCHOOL	FAMILY
• affect your brain	• lose friends	• make parents worry
• _____	• _____	• _____
• _____	• _____	• _____
• _____	• _____	• _____

PRESENT IDEAS
Use the frames to share ideas with your small group.

• One impact of drugs on your (health/school/family) is _____.

• Another consequence of drug use is _____.

• Using drugs can lead to _____.

Words to Know

BUILD WORD KNOWLEDGE

Rate your word knowledge. Then complete the chart for each topic-related word.

	① Don't Know	② Recognize	③ Familiar	④ Know

Word to Know	Meaning	Example
civil liberties *noun* ① ② ③ ④	the _____ of all people, such as their freedom of speech	Freedom of religion and the right to protest are civil liberties that _____ _____
confidential *adjective* ① ② ③ ④	meant to be kept _____	Leah told her friend that _____ _____ _____ but urged her to keep the news **confidential**.
deter *verb* ① ② ③ ④	to _____ from happening by threatening _____ _____	Knowing that _____ _____ **deters** me from _____
extracurricular *adjective* ① ② ③ ④	not part of the regular _____ _____ at school	_____ is one of the **extracurricular** activities that _____ _____
morale *noun* ① ② ③ ④	the level of _____ _____ and confidence that people have	_____ helped to raise the students' **morale** after a difficult school year.
privacy *noun* ① ② ③ ④	the state of being able to avoid _____ _____	My brother invades my **privacy** by _____
random *adjective* ① ② ③ ④	done or chosen without a specific _____ _____	To ensure fairness, _____ _____ will select our names at **random** to see _____ _____
target *verb* ① ② ③ ④	to _____ _____ toward a person, group, or thing	Ted does extra _____ to **target** _____ _____

Academic Discussion

Should schools be permitted to test students for drugs?

BRAINSTORM IDEAS

Briefly record at least two ideas.

Agree	Disagree

ANALYZE WORDS

Complete the chart with precise words to discuss and write about the issue.

Everyday	Precise
stop	prevent,
(drug) problem	dependency,
secret	classified,

MAKE A CLAIM

Rewrite two ideas using the frames and precise words.

1. **Frame:** From my point of view, schools (should/should not) be permitted to test for drugs if students _____ (**present-tense verb:** compete, participate, act).

   Response: _____

   _____

2. **Frame:** Considering _____ (**noun phrase:** the increase in, the impacts of), my stance is that schools (should/should not) be permitted to test students for drugs.

   Response: _____

   _____

   _____

COLLABORATE

Listen attentively, restate, and record your partner's idea.

Classmate's Name	Idea

Language to RESTATE
In other words, your stance is that _____.
Yes, that's accurate.
No. What I intended to say was _____.

Ten-Minute Paper

PRESENT IDEAS

Listen attentively, compare ideas, and take notes.
Then write whether you agree or disagree.

Classmate's Name	Idea	Agree/Disagree

ELABORATE IN WRITING

Work with the teacher to write a ten-minute paper.

> Considering the impacts of drug tests on students' behavior, my stance is that
> schools should be permitted to test students for drugs. For example, the threat of
> random drug testing might _____
> _____
> _____
>
> As a result, some students might avoid _____
> _____
> _____

Write a ten-minute paper.

> Considering _____
> _____ my stance is that schools
> _____ be permitted to test students for drugs.
> For example, _____
> _____
> _____
> As a result, _____
> _____
> _____
> _____

Words to Go

 BUILD WORD KNOWLEDGE

Complete the meaning and examples for this high-utility word.

Word to Go	Meaning	Examples
individual in·di·vid·u·al *noun*	one person, considered separately from a larger _____	Every individual should have the right to _____ _____ The individuals who started the fight were _____ _____

DISCUSS & WRITE EXAMPLES

Discuss your response with a partner. Then complete the sentence in writing.

As an **individual** who cares about _____ , I feel strongly that

_____

Write your response and read it aloud to a partner.

Thanks to some anonymous _____ who donated money, we

were able to _____

_____

BUILD WORD KNOWLEDGE

Complete the meaning and examples for this high-utility word.

Word to Go	Meaning	Examples
policy pol·i·cy *noun*	a _____	Our school has a **policy** against _____ _____ Many _____ disagreed with the school's **policies**, so they _____

DISCUSS & WRITE EXAMPLES

Discuss your response with a partner. Then complete the sentence in writing.

Our school's **policy** of _____ is fair because

_____

Write your response and read it aloud to a partner.

In his speech, the president outlined several new _____ on

_____

Language to Summarize

📖 BUILD FLUENCY
Read the article introduction and Section 1 (*Issues*, pp. 73–74).

💬 ASK & ANSWER QUESTIONS
Take turns asking and answering questions with a partner.

Q: What is this section **primarily about**?

A: This section is **primarily about** _____.

Q: What are the **most vital details** in this section?

A: One **vital detail** in this section is _____.

A: Another **vital detail** in this section is _____.

Section Shrink

 SUMMARIZE
Complete the topic and important details for Section 1. Then "shrink" the section by writing a summary in 35 or fewer words.

Topic (Who?/What?): preventing teen drug abuse versus violating constitutional rights

Important Details: • One major issue surrounding random student drug testing is

_____

• A national survey shows that _____

_____

• Opponents of random drug testing believe that _____

_____

Partner Summary: Supporters of student drug testing consider it _____

_____ ;

however, _____

_____

_____

Word Count: _____

Class Summary: _____

_____

_____

_____

_____

Word Count: _____

Words to Go

 BUILD WORD KNOWLEDGE

Complete the meanings and examples for this high-utility word.

Word to Go	Meanings	Examples
negative neg·a·tive *adjective*	bad or _____ ; not showing any sign of what _____ _____ _____ is looking for	One of the **negative** aspects of playing video games is _____ _____ John's test to check for _____ _____ produced **negative** results.

 DISCUSS & WRITE EXAMPLES

Discuss your response with a partner. Then complete the sentence in writing.

My mother warned me that _____

_____ could have a **negative** influence on me.

Write your response and read it aloud to a partner.

In science class, the result of _____

_____ was _____

 BUILD WORD KNOWLEDGE

Complete the meaning and examples for this high-utility word.

Word to Go	Meaning	Examples
potential po·ten·tial *adjective*	likely to _____ _____ something in the future	Nick saw a **potential** problem with his weekend plans when _____ _____ _____ The store clerk thought I was a **potential** customer, so she _____ _____ _____

 DISCUSS & WRITE EXAMPLES

Discuss your response with a partner. Then complete the sentence in writing.

In my opinion, **potential** teen drivers should be required to _____

_____ before they get their licenses.

Write your response and read it aloud to a partner.

Employers gather information about _____ employees by

_____

Language to Summarize

BUILD FLUENCY
Read Section 2 of the article (*Issues*, pp. 74–76).

ASK & ANSWER QUESTIONS
Take turns asking and answering questions with a partner.

Q: What does this section **address**?

A: This section **addresses** the (topic of/reasons for) _____.

Q: What are the **most compelling details** in this section?

A: One **compelling detail** in this section is _____.

A: Another **compelling detail** in this section is _____.

Section Shrink

SUMMARIZE
Complete the topic and important details for Section 2. Then "shrink" the section by writing a summary in 35 or fewer words.

Topic (Who?/What?):   reasons to _____

Important Details: • Proponents of drug testing maintain _____

_____

• One researcher commented that _____

_____

• _____

_____

Partner Summary: Advocates of drug testing claim _____

_____

_____

_____

_____

Word Count: _____

Class Summary: _____

_____

_____

_____

_____

Word Count: _____

Words to Go

 BUILD WORD KNOWLEDGE

Complete the meaning and examples for this high-utility word.

Word to Go	Meaning	Examples
method meth·od *noun*	a _____ _____ of doing something	If you can't _____ _____ you might try a different method of _____ Our teacher's **method** of encouraging students to _____ _____ involves _____ _____ _____

DISCUSS & WRITE EXAMPLES

Discuss your response with a partner. Then complete the sentence in writing.

_____

_____ is an effective **method** of reducing pollution in our city.

Write your response and read it aloud to a partner.

The _____ I use to prepare for a major test involves

_____

BUILD WORD KNOWLEDGE

Complete the meaning and examples for this high-utility word.

Word to Go	Meaning	Examples
strategy strat·e·gy *noun*	a _____ for making something happen	Our school's **strategy** for preventing _____ is to _____ _____ Rashid has two good **strategies** for _____ _____

DISCUSS & WRITE EXAMPLES

Discuss your response with a partner. Then complete the sentence in writing.

My **strategy** for winning the student council election is to _____

_____

Write your response and read it aloud to a partner.

Most magazines sell products by using persuasive _____, such as

_____

Quote Quest

BUILD FLUENCY
Read Section 3 of the article (*Issues*, pp. 76–77).

ANALYZE TEXT
Record a quote that supports or contradicts your position. Then use a frame to paraphrase the quote.

Quote: _____

_____

_____

_____

Paraphrase: _____

_____

_____

> **Language to PARAPHRASE**
>
> In this quote, the author provides a compelling (example of/reason for) _____.
>
> This quote makes it evident that _____.

SYNTHESIZE IDEAS
Write a topic sentence and two supporting sentences to respond to the quote.

Topic Sentence: I (agree/disagree) with the statement that _____.

_____

_____

_____

Supporting Sentence 1: (For example,/Drawing from my own experience,) _____.

_____

_____

Supporting Sentence 2: (As a result,/Consequently,) _____.

_____

_____

_____

COLLABORATE
Listen attentively as each member of your group reads a quote aloud. Then take turns using a frame to respond.

> **Language to RESPOND**
>
> This quote (supports/contradicts) my perspective.
>
> This statement took me by surprise.
>
> I found this quote astonishing.
>
> This statement resonated with me.

Student Writing Model

Academic Writing Type

An **argument** states a claim and supports it with reasons and evidence from sources.

    A. The **introduction** clearly states the writer's claim about the issue.
    B. **Detail paragraphs** support the claim with reasons and evidence. The
        writer may also present counterclaims and respond with strong evidence.
    C. The **conclusion** strongly restates the writer's claim about the issue.

⊕ ANALYZE TEXT

Read this student model to analyze the elements of an argument.

A

    After examining the issues surrounding mandatory drug testing, I disagree entirely that schools should test students for drugs.

B

    One reason I maintain this position is that drug testing does not educate students about drugs. In the article "Testing the Limits," Peter V. Smith and Mia Lee Velez emphasize that teen drug users simply shift to more harmful substances (76). As a teen, I have firsthand experience with the failures of drug testing. For instance, one peer has started experimenting with undetectable drugs. In contrast, the Supreme Court and many individuals have maintained that random testing deters drug use (Smith and Velez 76). However, I am convinced that schools do not have enough resources to identify all the drugs that teens use.

    Emily C. McKenna's analysis of drug testing in "Presumed Guilty" has strengthened my perspective that the policy unfairly targets teens. The article points out how student Loren Rasmussen felt that school administrators automatically treated him like a drug user (McKenna 80). Although a common argument in favor of drug testing is that it helps teens refuse drugs, I don't find the evidence believable. Clearly, there is adequate evidence that shows most teens already resist the pressure to experiment with drugs (Smith and Velez 75).

C

    The question of whether or not to permit drug testing in schools is complicated. My analysis of this issue has left me with little doubt that schools should not conduct student drug testing.

💬 MARK & DISCUSS ELEMENTS

Mark the argument elements and use the frames to discuss them with your partner.

1. **Underline the writer's claim.** *The writer's claim is that* _____.

2. **Check three reasons and four pieces of evidence that support the writer's claim.**
   One (reason/piece of evidence) that supports the writer's claim is _____.

3. **Draw boxes around two counterclaims.** *One counterclaim is* _____.

4. **Circle two verb phrases that express opinions.** *One verb phrase is* _____.

5. **Star seven precise topic words.** *An example of a precise topic word is* _____.

Choose Language for Writing

Prompt	Should schools be permitted to test students for drugs? Write an argument that states your claim and supports it with text evidence.

 GATHER TEXT EVIDENCE
Read Articles 2 and 3 in the *Issues* book (pp. 78–81).

 IDENTIFY PRECISE WORDS
Review the articles to identify precise words and phrases for your argument.

Article 1		Article 2	Article 3
• violates	• _____	• consequences	• community
• controversial	• _____	• individuals	• _____
• civil liberties	• _____	• _____	• _____
• _____	• _____	• _____	• _____
• _____	• _____	• _____	• _____

Organize Evidence and Counterclaims

 TAKE NOTES
Use academic language to state your claim and write an introduction.

Introduction: After examining the issues surrounding (topic) _____

_____

I (agree/disagree) _____ that (your claim) _____

_____

List two reasons that support your claim and evidence for each reason.

Reason 1: _____

Evidence: _____

_____

Reason 2: _____

Evidence: _____

_____

List two counterclaims and respond with strong evidence.

Counterclaim 1: _____

Response 1: _____

_____

Counterclaim 2: _____

Response 2: _____

_____

Present Perfect-Tense Verbs

Guidelines for Using Present Perfect-Tense Verbs

Present perfect-tense verbs show action that happened sometime in the past or action that has happened and is still happening. Use present perfect-tense verbs to provide data and anecdotal evidence from the text or your experience that supports your claim.

I **have watched** students protest against drug testing.	watch → have watched
Studies **have shown** that teen drug use can lead to addiction.	show → have shown
My friend **has refused** to submit to a drug test.	refuse → has refused
Many parents **have seen** what drugs can do to their children.	see → have seen

 IDENTIFY PRESENT PERFECT TENSE

Read the argument and circle the present perfect-tense verbs.

> After examining the issues surrounding teachers and drug testing, I am unconvinced that teachers should have to submit to drug tests in school.
>
> One reason I maintain this position is that research has shown that the costs may outweigh the benefits. In the magazine article, "Should School Districts Drug-Test Teachers?," John Cloud emphasizes that schools have struggled for years to raise money for testing. For example, school administrators have reported that for a school district in Ohio, a year of testing would cost $37,000 (Cloud 3). In contrast, School Board members have claimed that students are not the only individuals abusing drugs in schools (Cloud 5). However, I believe that schools need more realistic methods to deter substance abuse.
>
> Obi Achebe's analysis of teacher drug testing in "Schools Fall Apart" has strengthened my perspective that there are other underlying issues leading to the presence of drugs in schools. For example, most schools have cut their budgets drastically, leaving students with fewer extracurricular activities and teachers with reduced income (Achebe 12).
>
> The question of whether or not to require teacher drug testing is complex. My analysis of this issue has left me with little doubt that teacher drug testing should not be mandatory.

✏️ WRITE PRESENT PERFECT-TENSE VERBS

Complete the sentences with the present perfect tense of the verbs in parentheses.

1. Studies (*indicate*) _____ that 21.4 percent of eighth grade illicit drug users go on to have a lifetime habit.

2. Roughly 16.5 percent of U.S. schools (*conduct*) _____ random drug testing on their student population.

3. Every year, there (*be*) _____ a one percent increase in the number of schools testing students for drugs.

4. My parents and I (*reject*) _____ mandatory drug testing.

5. Our principal (*say*) _____ that she opposes the policy.

Paraphrasing Text

Guidelines for Paraphrasing Text
Look for a statement in a source text that supports your claim. Then **paraphrase** it by restating the idea using precise synonyms and your own words.

Source Text	Key Words & Phrases → Precise Synonyms		Paraphrasing
If a drug test is positive, the student takes follow-up tests and gets counseling. School officials notify parents or guardians but do not involve law enforcement.	if a drug test is positive → follow-up tests → gets → officials notify → parents or guardians → law enforcement →	positive test results further testing receives administrators contact family members the police	Positive test results lead to further testing, and the student receives counseling. School administrators contact family members but not the police.

IDENTIFY PRECISE SYNONYMS
Cross out key phrases in the sentences and replace them with precise synonyms.

1. Rasmussen's high school began a program of mandatory random drug testing in 2008 for students who participate in extracurricular activities, clubs, or sports and those who drive to school and park on campus.

2. Many students have refused random drug testing based on their beliefs. Some of those individuals have suffered for the decision.

3. There is one thing people on both sides of the issue agree on: drug-free schools and students.

PARAPHRASE IDEAS
Paraphrase the sentences above using your own words and precise synonyms.

1. For instance, _____

_____

2. The article states that _____

_____

_____

3. _____

_____

_____

Write an Argument

Prompt Should schools be permitted to test students for drugs? Write an argument that states your claim and supports it with text evidence.

 WRITE A RESEARCH PAPER
Use the frame to write your introduction, detail paragraphs, and conclusion.

A

After examining the issues surrounding _____
(topic)

I _____ that _____
(verb/verb phrase to express opinion)   (strongly state your claim)

_____

B

One reason I maintain this position is that _____
(first reason that supports your claim)

_____

In the article _____ , _____
(title of article)   (authors' full names)

emphasize that _____
(evidence from the article)

_____ As a teen, I have firsthand experience with

_____   _____
(situation or issue)   (Transition introducing evidence)

_____
(evidence from experience)

_____

In contrast, _____ _____
(group with an opposing claim)   (verb/verb phrase to express opinion)

that _____
(counterclaim from article or your experience)

However, I _____ that _____
(verb/verb phrase to express opinion)   (your response to counterclaim)

_____

_____ analysis of _____
(Author's full name + 's)   (topic)

in _____ has strengthened my perspective that
(title of a different article)

_____
(second reason that supports your claim)

_____   _____
(Transition introducing evidence)   (evidence from article or your experience)

Although a common argument _____ _____
(in favor of/against)   (issue)

is _____
(counterclaim from article or your experience)

I don't find the evidence _____ Clearly, there is _____
(precise adjective)   (adjective: sufficient, adequate, striking)

evidence that _____
(your response to the counterclaim)

C

The question of whether or not to _____
(restate the issue)

is _____ My analysis of this issue has left me with little doubt
(precise adjective to respond)

that _____
(restate your claim)

Rate Your Argument

ASSESS YOUR DRAFT
Rate your argument research paper. Then have a partner rate it.

Scoring Guide	
1	Insufficient
2	Developing
3	Sufficient
4	Exemplary

1. Does the introduction clearly state your claim?	Self	1	2	3	4
	Partner	1	2	3	4
2. Did you include strong reasons and evidence to support your claim?	Self	1	2	3	4
	Partner	1	2	3	4
3. Did you include counterclaims and respond with strong evidence?	Self	1	2	3	4
	Partner	1	2	3	4
4. Did you include precise topic words?	Self	1	2	3	4
	Partner	1	2	3	4
5. Did you include citation information for evidence from texts?	Self	1	2	3	4
	Partner	1	2	3	4
6. Did you use strong verbs and verb phrases to express opinions?	Self	1	2	3	4
	Partner	1	2	3	4
7. Did you include transitions to introduce reasons and evidence?	Self	1	2	3	4
	Partner	1	2	3	4
8. Did you include a variety of sentences (simple, compound, and complex)?	Self	1	2	3	4
	Partner	1	2	3	4

REFLECT & REVISE
Record specific priorities and suggestions to help you and your partner revise.

(Partner) Positive Feedback: I appreciated your (effort to/use of/skillful) _____

_____

_____

(Partner) Suggestion: As you revise your argument, make a point of _____

_____

_____

(Self) Priority 1: I plan to focus the revision of my argument on_____

_____

_____

(Self) Priority 2: One revision I plan to implement is to _____

_____

_____

✓ **CHECK & EDIT**
Use this checklist to proofread and edit your argument.

☐ Did you format citations correctly?

☐ Did you use commas appropriately after transitions?

☐ Did you use verb tenses appropriately?

☐ Are all words spelled correctly?

Should parents have a say in how their teens use social media?

 BUILD KNOWLEDGE
Read and respond to the Data File (*Issues*, p. 82).

 BRAINSTORM IDEAS
List groups of people who use social media, how they use it, and the risks.

SOCIAL MEDIA

USERS	ACTIVITIES	RISKS
• advertisers	• advertise product/services	• identity theft
• _____	• _____	• _____
• _____	• _____	• _____
• _____	• _____	• _____
• _____	• _____	• _____
• _____	• _____	• _____
• _____	• _____	• _____
• _____	• _____	• _____
• _____	• _____	• _____

 PRESENT IDEAS
Use the frames to share ideas with your small group.

• One example of a group that uses social media is _____.

• A risk of using social media is that _____.

• _____ use social media to _____.

Words to Know

 BUILD WORD KNOWLEDGE

Rate your word knowledge. Then complete the chart for each topic-related word.

① Don't Know	② Recognize	③ Familiar	④ Know

Word to Know	Meaning	Example
boundary *noun* ① ② ③ ④	the _____ of what is _____ _____ _____	My sister crossed a **boundary** when she _____ _____ _____
cautious *adjective* ① ② ③ ④	_____ about avoiding _____ _____	Because of the significant risks, teens need to be **cautious** about _____ _____
censor *verb* ① ② ③ ④	to _____ anything considered _____ or dangerous from a work of art or other text	One reason my parents try to **censor** music I listen to is _____ _____ _____
control *verb* ① ② ③ ④	to make someone or something _____ _____	My parents said that until I'm eighteen, they will **control** _____ _____
enforce *verb* ① ② ③ ④	to make people _____ a rule or law	At school, _____ _____ _____ **enforce** the rules about littering.
filter *verb* ① ② ③ ④	to use a computer program to _____ a website or remove _____	The computer lab uses special software to **filter** _____ _____ on the school computers.
protect *verb* ① ② ③ ④	to _____ _____ from harm or attack	_____ can **protect** me from _____ _____
reveal *verb* ① ② ③ ④	to make known something that was _____ _____ ; to _____	The tryout results should **reveal** which student will _____

Academic Discussion

Should parents control how their teens use social media?

 BRAINSTORM IDEAS

Briefly record at least two ideas.

Agree	Disagree

 ANALYZE WORDS

Complete the chart with precise words to discuss and write about the issue.

Everyday	Precise
be in charge of	supervise,
careful	vigilant,
keep safe	shield,

✏️ **MAKE A CLAIM**

Rewrite two ideas using the frames and precise words.

1. **Frame:** If their children have demonstrated _____ (**noun/noun phrase:** maturity, irresponsibility, the ability to), parents (should/should not) monitor their use of social media.

   Response: _____

   _____

2. **Frame:** I imagine that (some/many) parents are concerned about their children's use of social media due to _____ (**noun phrase:** the potential risks, the possibility of, the distraction from)

   Response: _____

   _____

 COLLABORATE

Listen attentively, restate, and record your partner's idea.

Classmate's Name	Idea

Language to RESTATE

So if I understand you correctly, your stance is that _____.

Yes, that's accurate.

No. What I intended to say was _____.

Ten-Minute Paper

PRESENT IDEAS

Listen attentively, compare ideas, and take notes.
Then write whether you agree or disagree.

Classmate's Name	Idea	Agree/Disagree

ELABORATE IN WRITING

Work with the teacher to write a ten-minute paper.

I imagine that some parents are concerned about their children's use of social media due to the potential risks it can pose for their futures. For example, many teens are not _____ about the photos they post of themselves. As a result, college recruiters or a potential employer may see those teens as _____ and may _____ _____ _____ _____

Write a ten-minute paper.

I imagine that _____ parents are concerned about their children's use of social media due to _____ _____

For example, _____ _____ _____

As a result, _____ _____ _____ _____ _____

Words to Go

 BUILD WORD KNOWLEDGE

Complete the meaning and examples for this high-utility word.

Word to Go	Meaning	Examples
communication com·mu·ni·ca·tion *noun*	the act of sharing _____ or expressing _____ _____	I _____ _____ to maintain communication with my friends. Communication with Lee is difficult because _____ _____ _____

DISCUSS & WRITE EXAMPLES

Discuss your response with a partner. Then complete the sentence in writing.

Frequent **communication** with my parents is important because _____

_____

Write your response and read it aloud to a partner.

In my family, most of our _____ involves _____

_____

 BUILD WORD KNOWLEDGE

Complete the meaning and examples for this high-utility word.

Word to Go	Meaning	Examples
security se·cu·ri·ty *noun*	the state of being free from _____ _____	Schools often have _____ _____ to improve **security** and prevent _____ _____ City officials increased **security** when _____ _____

DISCUSS & WRITE EXAMPLES

Discuss your response with a partner. Then complete the sentence in writing.

One way families can increase **security** in their homes is to _____

_____

Write your response and read it aloud to a partner.

I ensure my _____ online by _____

_____

Language to Summarize

📖 **BUILD FLUENCY**
Read the article introduction and Section 1 (*Issues*, pp. 83–84).

💬 **ASK & ANSWER QUESTIONS**
Take turns asking and answering questions with a partner.

Q: What is this section **primarily about**?

A: This section is **primarily about** _____.

Q: What are the most **vital details** in this section?

A: One **vital detail** in this section is _____.

A: Another **vital detail** in this section is _____.

Section Shrink

✏️ **SUMMARIZE**
Complete the topic and important details for Section 1. Then "shrink" the section by writing a summary in 35 or fewer words.

Topic (Who?/What?):   parents' fears of dangerous online interactions

Important Details: • More than 40 percent of teens _____

_____

• A 2006 study shows that _____

_____

• In 2009, _____

_____

• _____

_____

Partner Summary: Because a significant number of teens _____

_____

many parents _____

_____

Word Count: _____

Class Summary: _____

_____

_____

_____

Word Count: _____

Words to Go

BUILD WORD KNOWLEDGE

Complete the meaning and examples for this high-utility word.

Word to Go	Meaning	Examples
access ac·cess *noun*	the _____ to _____ _____ a place	Jamal needs **access** to the school library over the weekend because _____ _____ The school limited **access** to the _____ so that _____ _____ _____

DISCUSS & WRITE EXAMPLES

In my opinion, if teens had limited **access** to _____,

they would be more likely to _____

Write your response and read it aloud to a partner.

_____ might

provide teens greater _____ to jobs and career information.

BUILD WORD KNOWLEDGE

Complete the meaning and examples for this high-utility word.

Word to Go	Meaning	Examples
promote pro·mote *verb*	to _____ something become more _____ or well-known	As part of the social committee, Katy had to **promote** _____ _____ The neighborhood bookstore started a campaign to **promote** _____ _____

DISCUSS & WRITE EXAMPLES

Discuss your response with a partner. Then complete the sentence in writing.

If I wanted to sell tickets to _____, I would **promote** it by

_____

Write your response and read it aloud to a partner.

Fashion magazines use _____

_____

to try to _____ beauty products.

Language to Summarize

BUILD FLUENCY
Read Section 2 of the article (*Issues*, pp. 84–86).

ASK & ANSWER QUESTIONS
Take turns asking and answering questions with a partner.

Q: What does this section **address**?

A: This section **addresses** the (topic of/reasons for) _____.

Q: What are the most **compelling details** in this section?

A: One **compelling detail** in this section is _____.

A: Another **compelling detail** in this section is _____.

Section Shrink

 SUMMARIZE
Complete the topic and important details for Section 2. Then "shrink" the section by writing a summary in 35 or fewer words.

Topic (Who?/What?): how teens and parents _____

Important Details: • By 2006, Facebook _____

_____

• Many teens _____

_____ so they _____

• Parents are concerned that _____

_____

Partner Summary: Many teens _____

_____

however, parents _____

_____

Word Count: _____

Class Summary: _____

_____

_____

_____

_____

Word Count: _____

Words to Go

 BUILD WORD KNOWLEDGE
Complete the meaning and examples for this high-utility word.

Word to Go	Meaning	Examples
assume as·sume *verb*	to think that something is _____ without having definite _____	I **assumed** my mother was _____ _____ when I saw her _____ My family **assumes** I'm a bad cook just because I _____

DISCUSS EXAMPLES
Discuss your response with a partner. Then complete the sentence in writing.

Don't **assume** that _____

just because _____

BUILD WORD KNOWLEDGE
Complete the meaning and examples for this high-utility word.

Word to Go	Meaning	Examples
assumption as·sump·tion *noun*	a _____ that something is true without having definite _____	Pedro resents his mother's **assumption** that he _____ _____ just because he _____ I made the **assumption** that the temperature was warm because _____

DISCUSS EXAMPLES
Discuss your response with a partner. Then complete the sentence in writing.

I am basing my **assumption** that _____ on

the fact that _____

WRITE EXAMPLES
Write your response and read it aloud to a partner.

Your _____ that I _____

_____ because I care about the environment is absolutely correct.

I wish adults would stop _____ that all teens _____

_____

Quote Quest

BUILD FLUENCY

Read Section 3 of the article (*Issues*, pp. 86–87).

ANALYZE TEXT

Record a quote that supports or contradicts your position. Then use a frame to paraphrase the quote.

Quote: _____

_____

_____

_____

Paraphrase: _____

_____

_____

Language to PARAPHRASE
This quote makes it evident that _____.
In this quote, the author makes a case for _____.

SYNTHESIZE IDEAS

Write a topic sentence and two supporting sentences to respond to the quote.

Topic Sentence: I (agree/disagree) with the statement that _____.

_____

_____

_____

Supporting Sentence 1: (For example,/Drawing from my own experience,) _____.

_____

_____

_____

Supporting Sentence 2: (As a result,/Consequently,) _____.

_____

_____

_____

COLLABORATE

Listen attentively as each member of your group reads a quote aloud. Then take turns using a frame to respond.

Language to RESPOND
This quote validates my experience.
I found this quote astonishing.
This statement resonated with me.
This statement made me curious about _____.

Student Writing Model

Academic Writing Type

An **argument** states a claim and supports it with reasons and evidence from sources.

   A. The **introduction** clearly states the writer's claim about the issue.

   B. **Detail paragraphs** support the claim with reasons and evidence. The writer may also present counterclaims and respond with strong evidence.

   C. The **conclusion** strongly restates the writer's claim about the issue.

ANALYZE TEXT

Read this student model to analyze the elements of an argument.

A

After examining the issues surrounding teens and social media, I am convinced that parents should control how their teens use the Internet.

B

One reason I maintain this position is that teens need protection from online predators. In the article "Parents and Teens: Social Media Friends or Enemies?," Lucy Tang-Lessing emphasizes that "one in five young people experience unwanted sexual solicitations through social media sites" (84). As a teen, I have first-hand experience with cyber harassment. Among my peers, some friends receive inappropriate requests online. In contrast, critics maintain that most Internet solicitations come from other teens. However, I still contend that any interaction that threatens teens' security requires parental intervention.

Marisol Diaz's analysis of online monitoring in "Harlan Coben: Parent Spy" has strengthened my perspective that it is effective parenting. To illustrate, parents get involved when teens need help in the real world, so why not do the same with a social media threat? Although a common argument against parental control is that teens can take care of themselves, I don't find the evidence relevant. Clearly, there is strong evidence that shows why parents shouldn't make such assumptions about teens' safety (Diaz 89).

C

The question of whether or not parents should control their children's Internet use is difficult. My analysis of this issue has left me with little doubt that teens would benefit if parents monitored their online activities.

MARK & DISCUSS ELEMENTS

Mark the argument elements and use the frames to discuss them with your partner.

1. **Underline the writer's claim.** *The writer's claim is that _____.*

2. **Check three reasons and four pieces of evidence that support the writer's claim.**
   One (reason/piece of evidence) that supports the writer's claim is _____.

3. **Draw boxes around two counterclaims.** *One counterclaim is _____.*

4. **Circle two verb phrases that express opinions.** *One verb phrase is _____.*

5. **Star seven precise topic words.** *An example of a precise topic word is _____.*

Choose Language for Writing

Prompt	Should parents control how their teens use social media? Write an argument that states your claim and supports it with text evidence.

 GATHER TEXT EVIDENCE
Read Articles 2 and 3 in the *Issues* book (pp. 88–91).

 IDENTIFY PRECISE WORDS
Review the articles to identify precise words and phrases for your argument.

Article 1		Article 2	Article 3
• naïve	• _____	• parental responsibility	• the equivalent of
• interaction	• _____	• chilling	• _____
• revealed	• _____	• _____	• _____
• _____	• _____	• _____	• _____
• _____	• _____	• _____	• _____

Organize Evidence & Counterclaims

 TAKE NOTES
Use academic language to state your claim and write an introduction.

Introduction: After examining the issues surrounding (topic) _____

_____

I (agree/disagree) _____ that (your claim) _____

_____

List two reasons that support your claim and evidence for each reason.

Reason 1: _____

Evidence: _____

_____

Reason 2: _____

Evidence: _____

_____

List two counterclaims and respond with strong evidence.

Counterclaim 1: _____

Response 1: _____

_____

Counterclaim 2: _____

Response 2: _____

_____

Simple & Complex Sentences

Guidelines for Using Simple & Complex Sentences

Use **simple and complex sentences** to present and respond to counterclaims in your argument.

Presenting Counterclaims	Examples
A ____ (adjective: common, pervasive, consistent) argument (in favor of/against) ____ is ____.	**A pervasive argument against** video games is that they are addictive.
(Opponents/Proponents) of ____ tend to ____. (verb: emphasize, point out, highlight)	**Proponents of** banning plastic bags **tend to highlight** the animals harmed by the bags.
Although a common argument (in favor of/against) ____ is ____, I don't find the evidence ____. (adjective: compelling, substantial, believable)	**Although a common argument against** drug testing is that it presumes guilt, **I don't find the evidence compelling.**

Responding to Counterclaims	Examples
(Current data/Recent findings/Studies) actually demonstrate that ____.	**Studies actually demonstrate that** teens are more motivated to succeed in school if that will lead to obtaining a driver's license.
Clearly, there is (sufficient/adequate/striking) evidence that (shows/proves) ____.	**Clearly, there is adequate evidence that shows** a lower minimum wage creates more jobs.

✎ WRITE COUNTERCLAIMS

Work with the teacher to write a counterclaim and response.

Claim: Video games benefit teens.

Counterclaim: A (adjective: common, pervasive, consistent) _____ argument against video games is that they cause violence in teens.

Response: (Current data/Recent findings/Studies) _____ actually demonstrate that _____

Work with a partner to write a counterclaim and response.

Claim: Schools should not be permitted to test students for drugs.

Counterclaim: Although a common argument _____ is _____ I don't find the evidence _____

Response: Clearly, there is _____ evidence that _____

_____

Work on your own to write a counterclaim and response.

Claim: Media images do not harm teens.

Counterclaim: _____

_____

Response: _____

_____

Precise Language to Describe Evidence

Guidelines for Using Precise Language to Describe Evidence

Use **precise adjectives** and **noun phrases** to describe the data, statistics, and other evidence you present to support your claim.

Everyday Words	Precise Words/Phrases
good	convincing, strong, compelling, relevant, striking
scary	alarming, distressing, unnerving, striking, disturbing
new	recent, current, up-to-date
enough/true-sounding	sufficient, adequate, substantial, believable, convincing
a lot of/many/more	a/the high percentage of, a/the high number of, an/the increase in
little/less	a/the low percentage of, a/the decrease in, a/the limited number of

 WRITE PRECISE WORDS & PHRASES

Complete the sentences with precise adjectives and noun phrases.

1. One particularly _____ statistic is _____ _____ TV ads that encourage young girls to use beauty products.

2. Clearly, there is _____ evidence that shows _____ _____ crime in neighborhoods with graffiti.

3. Even though proponents of parental monitoring of social media use contend that _____ teens become victims of online predators, I do not consider this to be (a/an) _____ argument.

Use precise adjectives and noun phrases to complete the sentences about the claim.

Claim: The minimum wage should be the same for teens and adults.

1. **Evidence:** In the article "Help (Not) Wanted," Chris Alvarez and Julia Martinez present _____ data about the negative consequences of a lower minimum wage for teens.

2. **Evidence:** One particularly _____ fact is that _____ _____ teens' wages would make them feel undervalued.

3. **Counterclaim:** Although a common argument in favor of a reduced minimum wage is that it provides more job opportunities for teens, I don't find the evidence _____

4. **Response to Counterclaim:** Clearly, there is _____ evidence that shows getting paid less than adults reduces morale in teens.

5. **Restating Claim:** After reviewing _____ data and reflecting on my own experiences, I maintain that _____ _____

Write an Argument

Prompt | Should parents control how their teens use social media? Write an argument that states your claim and supports it with text evidence.

✏ WRITE A RESEARCH PAPER
Use the frame to write your introduction, detail paragraphs, and conclusion.

A

After examining the issues surrounding _____
(topic)

I _____ that _____
(verb/verb phrase to express opinion)   (strongly state your claim)

_____

B

One reason I maintain this position is that _____
(first reason that supports your claim)

_____

In the article _____
(title of article)

_____ emphasizes that _____
(author's full name)   (evidence from the article)

_____

As a teen, I have first-hand experience with _____
(situation or issue)

_____ _____
(Transition introducing evidence)   (evidence from experience)

_____

In contrast, _____ _____
(group with an opposing claim)   (verb/verb phrase to express opinion)

that _____
(counterclaim from article or your experience)

However, I _____ that _____
(verb/verb phrase to express opinion)   (your response to counterclaim)

_____

_____ analysis of _____
(Author's full name + 's)   (topic)

_____ in _____
(title of a different article)

has strengthened my perspective that _____
(second reason that supports your claim)

_____ _____
(Transition introducing evidence)   (evidence from article or your experience)

Although a common argument _____ _____
(in favor of/against)   (issue)

is _____
(counterclaim from article or your experience)

I don't find the evidence _____ Clearly, there is _____
(precise adjective to describe evidence)   (precise adjective to describe evidence)

evidence that _____ _____
(shows/proves)   (your response to the counterclaim)

C

The question of whether or not to _____
(restate the issue)

is _____ My analysis of this issue has left me with little doubt that
(precise adjective to respond)

_____
(restate your claim)

Rate Your Argument

ASSESS YOUR DRAFT
Rate your argument research paper. Then have a partner rate it.

Scoring Guide	
1	Insufficient
2	Developing
3	Sufficient
4	Exemplary

		1	2	3	4
1. Does the introduction clearly state your claim?	Self	1	2	3	4
	Partner	1	2	3	4
2. Did you include strong reasons and evidence to support your claim?	Self	1	2	3	4
	Partner	1	2	3	4
3. Did you include counterclaims and respond with strong evidence?	Self	1	2	3	4
	Partner	1	2	3	4
4. Did you include precise topic words?	Self	1	2	3	4
	Partner	1	2	3	4
5. Did you include citation information for evidence from texts?	Self	1	2	3	4
	Partner	1	2	3	4
6. Did you use strong verbs and verb phrases to express opinions?	Self	1	2	3	4
	Partner	1	2	3	4
7. Did you use precise adjectives to describe evidence?	Self	1	2	3	4
	Partner	1	2	3	4
8. Did you include transitions to introduce reasons and evidence?	Self	1	2	3	4
	Partner	1	2	3	4
9. Did you include complex sentences to present and respond to counterclaims?	Self	1	2	3	4
	Partner	1	2	3	4

REFLECT & REVISE
Record specific priorities and suggestions to help you and your partner revise.

(Partner) Positive Feedback: I appreciated your (effort to/use of/skillful) _____

_____

(Partner) Suggestion: As you revise your argument, make a point of _____

_____

(Self) Priority 1: I plan to focus the revision of my argument on _____

_____

_____

(Self) Priority 2: One revision I plan to implement is to _____

_____

_____

CHECK & EDIT
Use this checklist to proofread and edit your argument.

☐ Did you format citations correctly?

☐ Did you use commas appropriately after transitions?

☐ Did you use verb tenses appropriately?

☐ Are all words spelled correctly?

60-Second Speech

IDENTIFY TOPIC
Choose one of the questions below to address in a 60-second speech.

☐ What is the best way to prevent students from using drugs?

☐ Should social media sites require teens to have parental permission?

BRAINSTORM IDEAS
Write your claim and two reasons that support it.

My Claim: _____

Reason 1: _____

Reason 2: _____

SYNTHESIZE IDEAS
Take notes on supporting evidence and a counterclaim.

Evidence 1: _____

_____

Evidence 2: _____

_____

Counterclaim: _____

_____

Response: _____

_____

WRITE A SPEECH
Write a 60-second speech that states your claim and includes reasons, evidence, and a counterclaim.

I believe that _____

_____

One reason I maintain this position is that _____

_____

Secondly, _____

_____

To illustrate, _____

_____

The opposition might claim that _____

_____

However, _____

_____

For these reasons, I _____ that _____

_____

Present & Rate Your Speech

Using Gestures for Emphasis

A **gesture** is a silent body movement that expresses a feeling or idea. As you deliver your speech, use gestures at specific points, such as when you provide a surprising piece of evidence. A brief and appropriate gesture, such as a slight nod, emphasizes an important point and engages your audience.

PRESENT YOUR SPEECH

Present your speech to the small group. Make sure to use gestures for emphasis.

TAKE NOTES

Listen attentively to your classmates.
Take notes and write if you agree or disagree.

Language to AFFIRM & CLARIFY
That's a compelling point of view. Could you explain what you mean by _____?

Classmate's Name	Idea	Agree/ Disagree

ASSESS YOUR SPEECH

Use the Scoring Guide to rate your speech.

Scoring Guide			
1	Insufficient	3	Sufficient
2	Developing	4	Exemplary

	1	2	3	4
1. Did your topic sentence clearly state your claim?	1	2	3	4
2. Did you include strong reasons and evidence to support your speech?	1	2	3	4
3. Did you include precise topic words?	1	2	3	4
4. Did you use clear pronunciation?	1	2	3	4
5. Did you use gestures for emphasis?	1	2	3	4

REFLECT

Think of two ways you have improved on your speeches.

Praise 1: In my speeches, I was successful at _____

_____

_____

Praise 2: My greatest area of improvement was _____

_____

_____

Daily Do Now

Record the Daily Do Now at the beginning of class each day. Think carefully and complete the task using academic vocabulary and correct grammar.

	Complete Do Now	Use Vocabulary	Add Content	Correct Grammar	Total	
Date ____ / ____ / _____						Self
						Partner
Date ____ / ____ / _____						Self
						Partner
Date ____ / ____ / _____						Self
						Partner
Date ____ / ____ / _____						Self
						Partner
Date ____ / ____ / _____						Self
						Partner
Total Points						____ / 50

Scoring Guide

	Self	Partner
Did you/your partner **complete** the Daily Do Now?	+1	+1
Did you/your partner **use vocabulary** accurately?	+2	+1
Did you/your partner **add content** that is relevant?	+2	+1
Did you/your partner use **correct grammar**?	+1	+1

Scores

Complete Do Now	Use Vocabulary	Add Content	Correct Grammar	Total	

Date ____ / ____ / _____

| | | | | | Self |
| | | | | | Partner |

Date ____ / ____ / _____

| | | | | | Self |
| | | | | | Partner |

Date ____ / ____ / _____

| | | | | | Self |
| | | | | | Partner |

Date ____ / ____ / _____

| | | | | | Self |
| | | | | | Partner |

Date ____ / ____ / _____

| | | | | | Self |
| | | | | | Partner |

Insufficient	Developing	Admirable	Exceptional
0–50	51–70	71–90	91–100

Total Points ____ / 50

Grading Total ____ / 100

Daily Do Now

Record the Daily Do Now at the beginning of class each day. Think carefully and complete the task using academic vocabulary and correct grammar.

	Complete Do Now	Use Vocabulary	Add Content	Correct Grammar	Total	
Date ____ / ____ / _____						Self
						Partner
Date ____ / ____ / _____						Self
						Partner
Date ____ / ____ / _____						Self
						Partner
Date ____ / ____ / _____						Self
						Partner
Date ____ / ____ / _____						Self
						Partner
Total Points					____ / 50	

Scoring Guide

Scoring Guide	Self	Partner
Did you/your partner **complete** the Daily Do Now?	+1	+1
Did you/your partner **use vocabulary** accurately?	+2	+1
Did you/your partner **add content** that is relevant?	+2	+1
Did you/your partner use **correct grammar**?	+1	+1

Scores: Complete Do Now | Use Vocabulary | Add Content | Correct Grammar | Total

Date ____ / ____ / _____ — Self / Partner

Date ____ / ____ / _____ — Self / Partner

Date ____ / ____ / _____ — Self / Partner

Date ____ / ____ / _____ — Self / Partner

Date ____ / ____ / _____ — Self / Partner

Insufficient	Developing	Admirable	Exceptional
0–50	51–70	71–90	91–100

Total Points ____ / 50

Grading Total ____ / 100

Daily Do Now

Record the Daily Do Now at the beginning of class each day. Think carefully and complete the task using academic vocabulary and correct grammar.

	Complete Do Now	Use Vocabulary	Add Content	Correct Grammar	Total	
Scores						
Date ____ / ____ / _____						Self
						Partner
Date ____ / ____ / _____						Self
						Partner
Date ____ / ____ / _____						Self
						Partner
Date ____ / ____ / _____						Self
						Partner
Date ____ / ____ / _____						Self
						Partner
Total Points					____ / 50	

Scoring Guide	Self	Partner
Did you/your partner **complete** the Daily Do Now?	+1	+1
Did you/your partner **use vocabulary** accurately?	+2	+1
Did you/your partner **add content** that is relevant?	+2	+1
Did you/your partner use **correct grammar**?	+1	+1

	Complete Do Now	Use Vocabulary	Add Content	Correct Grammar	Total	
Date ___ / ___ / _____						Self
						Partner
Date ___ / ___ / _____						Self
						Partner
Date ___ / ___ / _____						Self
						Partner
Date ___ / ___ / _____						Self
						Partner
Date ___ / ___ / _____						Self
						Partner

Insufficient	Developing	Admirable	Exceptional
0–50	51–70	71–90	91–100

Total Points ___ / 50
Grading Total ___ / 100

Daily Do Now

Record the Daily Do Now at the beginning of class each day. Think carefully and complete the task using academic vocabulary and correct grammar.

	Complete Do Now	Use Vocabulary	Add Content	Correct Grammar	Total	
Date ____ / ____ / _____						Self
						Partner
Date ____ / ____ / _____						Self
						Partner
Date ____ / ____ / _____						Self
						Partner
Date ____ / ____ / _____						Self
						Partner
Date ____ / ____ / _____						Self
						Partner
Total Points						____ / 50

Scoring Guide

Scoring Guide	Self	Partner
Did you/your partner **complete** the Daily Do Now?	+1	+1
Did you/your partner **use vocabulary** accurately?	+2	+1
Did you/your partner **add content** that is relevant?	+2	+1
Did you/your partner use **correct grammar**?	+1	+1

Scores: Complete Do Now | Use Vocabulary | Add Content | Correct Grammar | Total

Date ____ / ____ / _____ — Self / Partner

Date ____ / ____ / _____ — Self / Partner

Date ____ / ____ / _____ — Self / Partner

Date ____ / ____ / _____ — Self / Partner

Date ____ / ____ / _____ — Self / Partner

Insufficient	Developing	Admirable	Exceptional
0–50	51–70	71–90	91–100

Total Points ____ / 50

Grading Total ____ / 100

Daily Do Now

Record Daily Do Now at the beginning of class each day. Think carefully and complete the task using academic vocabulary and correct grammar.

	Complete Do Now	Use Vocabulary	Add Content	Correct Grammar	Total	
Scores						
Date ___ / ___ / ___						Self
						Partner
Date ___ / ___ / ___						Self
						Partner
Date ___ / ___ / ___						Self
						Partner
Date ___ / ___ / ___						Self
						Partner
Date ___ / ___ / ___						Self
						Partner
Total Points						___ / 50

Scoring Guide

	Self	Partner
Did you/your partner **record** the Daily Do Now?	+1	+1
Did you/your partner **use vocabulary** accurately?	+2	+1
Did you/your partner **add content** that is relevant?	+2	+1
Did you/your partner use **correct grammar**?	+1	+1

Scores				
Complete Do Now	Use Vocabulary	Add Content	Correct Grammar	Total

Date _____ / _____ / _____

Self / Partner

Date _____ / _____ / _____

Self / Partner

Date _____ / _____ / _____

Self / Partner

Date _____ / _____ / _____

Self / Partner

Date _____ / _____ / _____

Self / Partner

Insufficient	Developing	Admirable	Exceptional
0–50	51–70	71–90	91–100

Total Points _____ / 50
Grading Total _____ / 100

Daily Do Now

Record the Daily Do Now at the beginning of class each day. Think carefully and complete the task using academic vocabulary and correct grammar.

	Complete Do Now	Use Vocabulary	Add Content	Correct Grammar	Total	
Scores						
Date ____ / ____ / _____						Self
						Partner
Date ____ / ____ / _____						Self
						Partner
Date ____ / ____ / _____						Self
						Partner
Date ____ / ____ / _____						Self
						Partner
Date ____ / ____ / _____						Self
						Partner
Total Points						____ / 50

Scoring Guide

	Self	Partner
Did you/your partner **complete** the Daily Do Now?	+1	+1
Did you/your partner **use vocabulary** accurately?	+2	+1
Did you/your partner **add content** that is relevant?	+2	+1
Did you/your partner use **correct grammar**?	+1	+1

	Scores					
	Complete Do Now	Use Vocabulary	Add Content	Correct Grammar	Total	
Date ____ / ____ / _____						Self
						Partner
Date ____ / ____ / _____						Self
						Partner
Date ____ / ____ / _____						Self
						Partner
Date ____ / ____ / _____						Self
						Partner
Date ____ / ____ / _____						Self
						Partner

Insufficient	Developing	Admirable	Exceptional
0–50	51–70	71–90	91–100

Total Points _____ / 50

Grading Total _____ / 100

Daily Do Now

Record the Daily Do Now at the beginning of class each day. Think carefully and complete the task using academic vocabulary and correct grammar.

	Scores					
	Complete Do Now	Use Vocabulary	Add Content	Correct Grammar	Total	

Date ____ / ____ / _____						
						Self
						Partner

Date ____ / ____ / _____						
						Self
						Partner

Date ____ / ____ / _____						
						Self
						Partner

Date ____ / ____ / _____						
						Self
						Partner

Date ____ / ____ / _____						
						Self
						Partner

Total Points _____ / 50

Scoring Guide

Scoring Guide	Self	Partner
Did you/your partner **complete** the Daily Do Now?	+1	+1
Did you/your partner **use vocabulary** accurately?	+2	+1
Did you/your partner **add content** that is relevant?	+2	+1
Did you/your partner use **correct grammar**?	+1	+1

Scores: Complete Do Now, Use Vocabulary, Add Content, Correct Grammar, Total

Date _____ / _____ / _____ — Self / Partner

Date _____ / _____ / _____ — Self / Partner

Date _____ / _____ / _____ — Self / Partner

Date _____ / _____ / _____ — Self / Partner

Date _____ / _____ / _____ — Self / Partner

Insufficient	Developing	Admirable	Exceptional
0–50	51–70	71–90	91–100

Total Points _____ / 50

Grading Total _____ / 100

Daily Do Now

Record the Daily Do Now at the beginning of class each day. Think carefully and complete the task using academic vocabulary and correct grammar.

	Complete Do Now	Use Vocabulary	Add Content	Correct Grammar	Total	
	Scores					
Date ____ / ____ / _____						Self
						Partner
Date ____ / ____ / _____						Self
						Partner
Date ____ / ____ / _____						Self
						Partner
Date ____ / ____ / _____						Self
						Partner
Date ____ / ____ / _____						Self
						Partner
Total Points					____ / 50	

Scoring Guide

Scoring Guide	Self	Partner
Did you/your partner **complete** the Daily Do Now?	+1	+1
Did you/your partner **use vocabulary** accurately?	+2	+1
Did you/your partner **add content** that is relevant?	+2	+1
Did you/your partner use **correct grammar**?	+1	+1

Scores

	Complete Do Now	Use Vocabulary	Add Content	Correct Grammar	Total	
Date ____ / ____ / _____						Self
						Partner
Date ____ / ____ / _____						Self
						Partner
Date ____ / ____ / _____						Self
						Partner
Date ____ / ____ / _____						Self
						Partner
Date ____ / ____ / _____						Self
						Partner

Insufficient	Developing	Admirable	Exceptional
0–50	51–70	71–90	91–100

Total Points _____ / 50

Grading Total _____ / 100

Daily Do Now

Record the Daily Do Now at the beginning of class each day. Think carefully and complete the task using academic vocabulary and correct grammar.

	Complete Do Now	Use Vocabulary	Add Content	Correct Grammar	Total	
Scores						
Date ____ / ____ / _____						Self
						Partner
Date ____ / ____ / _____						Self
						Partner
Date ____ / ____ / _____						Self
						Partner
Date ____ / ____ / _____						Self
						Partner
Date ____ / ____ / _____						Self
						Partner
Total Points						____ / 50

Scoring Guide

	Self	Partner
Did you/your partner **complete** the Daily Do Now?	+1	+1
Did you/your partner **use vocabulary** accurately?	+2	+1
Did you/your partner **add content** that is relevant?	+2	+1
Did you/your partner use **correct grammar**?	+1	+1

Scores: Complete Do Now | Use Vocabulary | Add Content | Correct Grammar | Total

Date _____ / _____ / _____   Self / Partner

Date _____ / _____ / _____   Self / Partner

Date _____ / _____ / _____   Self / Partner

Date _____ / _____ / _____   Self / Partner

Date _____ / _____ / _____   Self / Partner

Insufficient	Developing	Admirable	Exceptional
0–50	51–70	71–90	91–100

Total Points _____ / 50
Grading Total _____ / 100

Daily Do Now

Record the Daily Do Now at the beginning of class each day. Think carefully and complete the task using academic vocabulary and correct grammar.

	Complete Do Now	Use Vocabulary	Add Content	Correct Grammar	Total	
Date ___ / ___ / _____						Self
						Partner
Date ___ / ___ / _____						Self
						Partner
Date ___ / ___ / _____						Self
						Partner
Date ___ / ___ / _____						Self
						Partner
Date ___ / ___ / _____						Self
						Partner

Total Points _____ / 50

Scoring Guide

	Self	Partner
Did you/your partner **complete** the Daily Do Now?	+1	+1
Did you/your partner **use vocabulary** accurately?	+2	+1
Did you/your partner **add content** that is relevant?	+2	+1
Did you/your partner use **correct grammar**?	+1	+1

Scores				
Complete Do Now	Use Vocabulary	Add Content	Correct Grammar	Total

Date _____ / _____ / _____

Self

Partner

Date _____ / _____ / _____

Self

Partner

Date _____ / _____ / _____

Self

Partner

Date _____ / _____ / _____

Self

Partner

Date _____ / _____ / _____

Self

Partner

Insufficient	Developing	Admirable	Exceptional
0–50	51–70	71–90	91–100

Total Points _____ / 50

Grading Total _____ / 100

Daily Do Now

Record the Daily Do Now at the beginning of class each day. Think carefully and complete the task using academic vocabulary and correct grammar.

	Scores					
	Complete Do Now	Use Vocabulary	Add Content	Correct Grammar	Total	

Date ____ / ____ / _____ _____ _____						Self
_____ _____						Partner
Date ____ / ____ / _____ _____ _____						Self
_____ _____						Partner
Date ____ / ____ / _____ _____ _____						Self
_____ _____						Partner
Date ____ / ____ / _____ _____ _____						Self
_____ _____						Partner
Date ____ / ____ / _____ _____ _____						Self
_____ _____						Partner

Total Points ____ / 50

Scoring Guide

	Self	Partner
Did you/your partner **complete** the Daily Do Now?	+1	+1
Did you/your partner **use vocabulary** accurately?	+2	+1
Did you/your partner **add content** that is relevant?	+2	+1
Did you/your partner use **correct grammar**?	+1	+1

Scores

Complete Do Now | Use Vocabulary | Add Content | Correct Grammar | Total

Date _____ / _____ / _____

_____

_____

_____

Self

Partner

Date _____ / _____ / _____

_____

_____

_____

Self

Partner

Date _____ / _____ / _____

_____

_____

_____

Self

Partner

Date _____ / _____ / _____

_____

_____

_____

Self

Partner

Date _____ / _____ / _____

_____

_____

_____

Self

Partner

Insufficient	Developing	Admirable	Exceptional
0–50	51–70	71–90	91–100

Total Points _____ / 50

Grading Total _____ / 100

Daily Do Now

Record the Daily Do Now at the beginning of class each day. Think carefully and complete the task using academic vocabulary and correct grammar.

	Scores					
	Complete Do Now	Use Vocabulary	Add Content	Correct Grammar	Total	
Date ____ / ____ / _____						Self
						Partner
Date ____ / ____ / _____						Self
						Partner
Date ____ / ____ / _____						Self
						Partner
Date ____ / ____ / _____						Self
						Partner
Date ____ / ____ / _____						Self
						Partner
Total Points						____ / 50

Scoring Guide

	Self	Partner
Did you/your partner **complete** the Daily Do Now?	+1	+1
Did you/your partner **use vocabulary** accurately?	+2	+1
Did you/your partner **add content** that is relevant?	+2	+1
Did you/your partner use **correct grammar**?	+1	+1

Scores

Complete Do Now | Use Vocabulary | Add Content | Correct Grammar | Total

Date _____ / _____ / _____ — Self / Partner

Date _____ / _____ / _____ — Self / Partner

Date _____ / _____ / _____ — Self / Partner

Date _____ / _____ / _____ — Self / Partner

Date _____ / _____ / _____ — Self / Partner

Insufficient	Developing	Admirable	Exceptional
0–50	51–70	71–90	91–100

Total Points _____ / 50
Grading Total _____ / 100

Daily Do Now

Record the Daily Do Now at the beginning of class each day. Think carefully and complete the task using academic vocabulary and correct grammar.

	Complete Do Now	Use Vocabulary	Add Content	Correct Grammar	Total	
Scores						
Date ____ / ____ / _____						Self
						Partner
Date ____ / ____ / _____						Self
						Partner
Date ____ / ____ / _____						Self
						Partner
Date ____ / ____ / _____						Self
						Partner
Date ____ / ____ / _____						Self
						Partner
Total Points					____ / 50	

Scoring Guide

Scoring Guide	Self	Partner
Did you/your partner **complete** the Daily Do Now?	+1	+1
Did you/your partner **use vocabulary** accurately?	+2	+1
Did you/your partner **add content** that is relevant?	+2	+1
Did you/your partner use **correct grammar**?	+1	+1

Scores					
Complete Do Now	Use Vocabulary	Add Content	Correct Grammar	Total	

Date _____ / _____ / _____

_____

_____

_____

_____

Self

Partner

Date _____ / _____ / _____

_____

_____

_____

_____

Self

Partner

Date _____ / _____ / _____

_____

_____

_____

_____

Self

Partner

Date _____ / _____ / _____

_____

_____

_____

_____

Self

Partner

Date _____ / _____ / _____

_____

_____

_____

_____

Self

Partner

Insufficient	Developing	Admirable	Exceptional
0–50	51–70	71–90	91–100

Total Points _____ / 50

Grading Total _____ / 100